THE ULTIMATE TRUE CRIME TRIVIA

330 INTRIGUING QUESTIONS & ANSWERS

K. Murdle

330 ULTIMATE TRUE CRIME TRIVIA:

Intriguing Questions and Answers

PAPERBACK ISBN: 978-969-5492-75-8

EXCLUSIVE BONUS!

Scan This Code to GET FREE COPIES of
500 SERIAL KILLERS Encyclopedia
Original SERIAL KILLERS Trivia BOOK
THE ULTIMATE TRUE CRIME TRIVIA

TABLE OF CONTENTS

INTRODUCTION

Welcome, brave reader, to the darkest corners of the human psyche. Here you will read about the most famous serial killers and the not so famous ones. *The ULTIMATE Serial Killers TRIVIA: Intriguing Questions and Answers* is not just a book—it's a journey into the minds of the most chilling individuals ever to walk among us. If you think you know fear, prepare to have your perceptions shattered. This is not for the faint of heart. This is for those who dare to peer into the abyss, knowing that the abyss might just peer back.

Serial killers—they lurk in the shadows, hidden behind friendly smiles and ordinary lives. They could be anyone: the charming neighbor, the helpful coworker, or the unassuming stranger who passes you on the street. What drives these predators? How do they choose their victims? And more importantly, could you spot one if you saw them?

In this compendium of chilling trivia, we delve deep into the macabre world of serial killers. We'll uncover their twisted methods, explore the sinister patterns that connect them, and challenge everything you thought you knew about the darkest aspects of humanity.

What Drives a Serial Killer?

Understanding what makes a serial killer tick is a question that has tormented psychologists, criminologists, and the public alike. Is it nature or nurture? Are killers born with a predisposition to murder, or are they molded by their environments? The answer isn't straightforward.

Many serial killers share common traits rooted in their childhoods. Abuse, neglect, and trauma often lay the foundation for future violence. Patterns emerge: cruelty to animals, bed-wetting beyond the typical age, and a fascination with fire. These behaviors, known as the Macdonald triad, are not definitive predictors but serve as red flags.

Yet, not everyone who experiences a troubled upbringing becomes a murderer. The human psyche is complex, and the path to becoming a serial killer involves a convergence of factors that we are only beginning to understand. This book delves into these elements, offering insights into the minds behind the madness.

Methods of Murder

Serial killers employ a variety of methods to end lives, each choice reflecting something about their psyche. Firearms are common—quick, efficient, and detached. Pulling a trigger allows for a degree of emotional distance. But for some killers, that's not enough.

Stabbings offer a grim intimacy. The killer feels the blade pierce flesh, witnesses the life drain from their victim up close. It's personal, brutal, and satisfies a different kind of compulsion. Strangulation is similar—requiring physical contact and strength, it prolongs the act, extending the killer's sense of control and dominance.

Poisoning presents another method, often associated with cunning and premeditation. It allows the killer to act from the shadows, manipulating without direct confrontation. While historically linked to female perpetrators, male killers like Dr. Michael Swango have also used poison to deadly effect, observing their victims' suffering with detached curiosity.

Each method tells a story about the killer's desires and motivations. As you explore the cases in this book, consider what their chosen means of murder reveal about them.

Origins of Evil

The United States holds a notorious reputation for producing a significant number of serial killers. While these predators exist worldwide, America has been the backdrop for many of the most infamous cases. Cultural, social, and economic factors contribute to this grim statistic, but the reasons are multifaceted and complex.

Serial killers come from all walks of life, defying easy categorization. Some were raised in stable homes, while others endured unimaginable hardships. What they share is a divergence from empathy and a descent into darkness that most of us cannot fathom.

This book not only examines killers from the United States but also brings to light international cases. By comparing and contrasting these individuals, we aim to shed light on the universal and unique aspects of their crimes.

Who Are Actually Serial Killers?

Not all multiple murderers are serial killers. Understanding the distinctions is crucial.

A **mass murderer** kills multiple people in a single event or location. Their acts are often impulsive, driven by immediate rage or ideology. Take James Holmes, who opened fire in a crowded movie theater in Aurora, Colorado. His attack was sudden, with no intention of prolonging the terror beyond that moment.

Then there are **spree killers**, who commit multiple murders in different locations over a short period. Their rampages are continuous, with little time between attacks. Christopher Dorner's vengeance-fueled killings after being fired from the LAPD exemplify this. He moved quickly, leaving a trail of death before ultimately taking his own life.

A **serial killer**, however, murders three or more people over an extended period, with cooling-off intervals in between. These pauses distinguish them from spree killers and indicate a return to normalcy—or at least the appearance of it—between crimes. Ted Bundy is a quintessential example, charming and intelligent, he evaded capture while killing numerous women across several states.

Serial killers often plan meticulously, stalking their victims and selecting them based on specific criteria. Their killings fulfill psychological needs, whether it's power, control, sexual gratification, or a twisted ideological belief.

The Reason for Undertaking This Hunt

What compels us to study serial killers? There's a morbid fascination with the extremes of human behavior. They operate outside the boundaries of societal norms, challenging our understanding of morality and humanity.

By examining their lives and crimes, we hope to find answers—signs we might have missed, interventions that could have prevented tragedy. This pursuit is not just academic; it's a quest for safety and prevention. If we can unravel the mysteries of their minds, perhaps we can stop the next killer before they strike.

Inside This Book

"The ULTIMATE Serial Killers TRIVIA" is more than a compilation of questions and answers. It's an exploration of the darkest corners of human behavior. Each chapter delves into different aspects of serial killers—their methods, motives, backgrounds, and the investigations that led to their capture.

You'll encounter well-known figures like Jeffrey Dahmer and lesser-known but equally terrifying killers from around the globe. Test your knowledge, challenge your assumptions, and prepare to confront the unsettling reality that monsters sometimes wear familiar faces.

A Word of Caution

This journey is not for the faint of heart. The content is disturbing, the facts gruesome. But knowledge is a powerful tool. By facing the horrors head-on, we empower ourselves to recognize danger and advocate for vigilance.

Serial killers represent a fracture in the human condition, a deviation that provokes fear and curiosity. They force us to question the nature of evil and the capacity for darkness within us all.

As you delve into this book, remember that each question answered brings us one step closer to understanding. Each fact uncovered shines a light into the shadows where such evil thrives.

Are you ready to confront the unsettling truths that await? Turn the page, and let's begin this chilling exploration together.

TRIVIA QUESTIONS

1. **BEHIND THE CHEERFUL FACADE, WHAT DARK SECRET DID POGO THE CLOWN CONCEAL?**

A. He was a bank robber.
B. He was involved in a drug smuggling ring.
C. He was a serial killer who preyed on young boys.
D. He was leading a double life as a spy.

2. **TRUE OR FALSE: A LARGE NUMBER OF BELGIANS WITH THE SURNAME "DUTROUX" CHANGED THEIR NAMES DUE TO THE OUTRAGE OVER MARC DUTROUX'S CRIMES.**

A. True
B. False

3. **WHICH FACT IS TRUE ABOUT JUANA BARRAZA, THE MEXICAN SERIAL KILLER?**

A. She targeted men who reminded her of her father
B. She was a professional wrestler
C. She maintained her innocence until the end
D. She prepared meals for her victims before killing them

4. **WHO SENT A POTENTIAL VICTIM A POEM AND HER BELONGINGS AFTER STAKING OUT HER HOME?**

A. Gary Ridgway
B. Dennis Rader
C. Leonard Lake
D. The Long Island Serial Killer

5. **WHICH SOCIAL MEDIA PLATFORM DID A JAPANESE SERIAL KILLER USE TO TARGET HIS VICTIMS?**

A. TikTok
B. WeChat

C. Facebook
D. Twitter

6. HOW DID CLIVE EXPECT TO DO IF JACK THE RIPPER WAS SELECTED BY THE SPINNER?

A. By injecting them with poison
B. By mutilating them with a knife
C. By eviscerating them and using Masonic symbols
D. By leaving them to die in the cold

7. WHAT MADE CLIVE DISCARD HIS HOPE OF MIMICKING A SERIAL KILLER'S CRIMES AT THAT MOMENT?

A. Fear of getting caught
B. Realizing he was brooding too much
C. A sudden loss of interest
D. Hearing a warning from Derek

8. WHAT DID CLIVE THINK WAS THE MOST AWESOME SERIAL KILLER NICKNAME AFTER THE 'KILLER CLOWN'?

A. The Phantom Strangler
B. The Eyeball Killer
C. The Shadow Butcher
D. The Night Stalker

9. WHAT DID SERIAL KILLER ISRAEL KEYES AND GARY GILMORE HAVE IN COMMON?

A. Both were executed by firing squad
B. They both wanted a swift execution
C. They were childhood friends
D. They attended the same high school

10. WHOSE ADOLESCENT SON HELPED THEM CARRY OUT THEIR CRIMES?

A. Robert Black
B. Velma Barfield

C. Joseph Kallinger
D. Gary Ridgway

11. TRUE OR FALSE: TWO OF COLOMBIA'S MOST INFAMOUS SERIAL KILLERS, PEDRO ALONSO LÓPEZ AND DANIEL CAMARGO BARBOSA, WERE ONCE IMPRISONED TOGETHER.

A. True
B. False

12. WHICH KILLERS WERE RELEASED FROM PRISON ONLY TO MURDER AGAIN?

A. Kenneth McDuff
B. Arthur Shawcross
C. Edmund Kemper
D. All of the above

13. WHICH SERIAL KILLER CASE REMAINS UNSOLVED?

A. Stoneman
B. Butcher of Jombang
C. Honolulu Strangler
D. Both A and C

14. TRUE OR FALSE: A LEGENDARY SERIAL KILLER FROM STATEN ISLAND TURNED OUT TO BE A REAL PERSON.

A. True
B. False

15. WHAT CHILLING RITUAL DID TED BUNDY PERFORM WITH THE BODIES OF HIS VICTIMS?

A. He posed them in elaborate tableaux.
B. He took photographs of them in staged scenes.
C. He revisited them for necrophilic acts.
D. He dressed them in different outfits.

16. WHICH COMMON MISCONCEPTION ABOUT SERIAL KILLERS DOESN'T MATCH REALITY?

A. Most serial killers are loners
B. Most serial killers are always male
C. Most serial killers prefer poison
D. Most serial killers have mental disorders

17. WHAT MAKES SERIAL KILLERS LIKE DENIS RADER AND GARY RIDGEWAY ESPECIALLY FRIGHTENING?

A. They were highly intelligent masterminds
B. They were capable of hiding in plain sight while living normal lives
C. They always worked alone and left no evidence
D. They confessed to all their crimes immediately

18. WHAT DID ROBERT HANSEN, KNOWN AS THE BUTCHER BAKER, DO TO HIS VICTIMS IN THE ALASKAN WILDERNESS?

A. He let them go after torturing them
B. He forced them into gladiator-style fights
C. He released them into the wilderness and hunted them like animals
D. He drugged them and left them unconscious in the forest

19. HOW MANY WOMEN DID ROBERT HANSEN KILL, ACCORDING TO RECORDS?

A. At least 10
B. Over 20
C. At least 17
D. More than 50

20. WHY DID JEFFREY DAHMER KILL HIS VICTIMS?

A. For money
B. To create mindless sex slaves
C. For revenge
D. To cover up a crime

21. WHAT LED TO JEFFREY DAHMER BEING CAUGHT?

A. His car was identified
B. A neighbor reported suspicious smells
C. He was caught during a murder
D. A victim escaped and alerted police

22. WHO WAS THE 'NIGHT STALKER'?

A. David Berkowitz
B. Dennis Rader
C. Richard Ramirez
D. Charles Manson

23. WHO BUILT A MURDER CASTLE IN CHICAGO?

A. Ed Gein
B. H.H. Holmes
C. Albert Fish
D. Peter Kürten

24. WHAT DID POLICE FIND IN ED GEIN'S HOME?

A. Human remains buried in the backyard
B. A belt made from female nipples
C. A dungeon filled with torture devices
D. Dozens of guns and weapons

25. WHAT MISTAKE DID POLICE MAKE THAT LED TO KONERAK SINTHASOMPHONE'S DEATH?

A. They arrested the wrong person
B. They ignored complaints from neighbors
C. They allowed Dahmer to take him back to his apartment
D. They failed to follow up on a missing person's report

26. WHAT WAS RICHARD RAMIREZ'S ATTITUDE TOWARD HIS CRIMES AND PUNISHMENT?

A. He begged for forgiveness
B. He claimed innocence
C. He was defiant and unremorseful
D. He escaped prison multiple times

27. WHAT WAS THE PRIMARY MOTIVATION FOR H.H. HOLMES' MURDERS?

A. To steal valuables
B. Financial gain through insurance fraud
C. Sexual gratification
D. Revenge against his enemies

28. WHO WAS JACK THE RIPPER?

A. A London police officer
B. A surgeon in Victorian England
C. An unidentified serial killer
D. A nobleman

29. WHAT WAS ELIZABETH BATHORY KNOWN FOR?

A. Poisoning her enemies
B. Murdering young women
C. Assassinating political rivals
D. Stealing royal jewels

30. WHAT WERE CARL PANZRAM'S LAST WORDS?

A. "I regret nothing."
B. "May you all burn in hell."
C. "I wish the world had one neck so I could choke it."
D. "I forgive everyone."

31. WHICH SERIAL KILLER HAD AN OPERA MADE ABOUT HER LIFE?

A. Aileen Wuornos
B. Lizzie Borden
C. Belle Gunness
D. Myra Hindley

32. WHAT DID ED KEMPER DO TO HIS MOTHER AFTER HE KILLED HER?

A. Set her body on fire
B. Buried her in the garden
C. Used her head as a dartboard
D. Threw her in a river

33. HOW DID THE GREEN RIVER KILLER EARN HIS NAME?

A. He wore green clothing during his murders
B. He left his victims near the Green River
C. He painted his crime scenes green
D. He carved a green symbol on his victims

34. DID LARRY HALL'S TWIN BROTHER HELP HIM WITH HIS MURDERS?

A. Yes, they worked together
B. No, but his brother knew about them
C. No, he had no involvement
D. Possibly, but it was never proven

35. WHO DID THE LEADER OF THE CHICAGO RIPPER CREW ONCE WORK FOR?

A. Richard Speck
B. Anthony Sowell
C. John Wayne Gacy
D. Keith Jesperson

36. WHICH SERIAL KILLER WAS CAUGHT AFTER BODY PARTS CLOGGED A DRAIN?

A. Robert Pickton
B. Dennis Nilsen
C. Dean Corll
D. Dr. Harold Shipman

37. WHICH OF THE FOLLOWING IS TRUE ABOUT THE BLOODY BENDERS, A FAMILY OF KANSAS-BASED KILLERS?

A. They murdered at least 11 people
B. Daughter Kate claimed to be a psychic
C. They were never caught
D. All of the above

38. WHICH ITEM HELPED FORENSIC SCIENTISTS CONNECT A JACK THE RIPPER SUSPECT IN 2019?

A. Annie Chapman's shoe
B. Catherine Eddowes' shawl
C. Mary Jane Kelly's handkerchief
D. Mary Ann Nichols' skirt

39. WHAT DID FBI AGENTS ONCE TELL CRIMINOLOGIST DR. ERIC HICKEY?

A. All serial killers have a signature
B. Only white males become serial killers
C. Female serial killers don't exist
D. All serial killers can be rehabilitated

40. WHAT SAVED A WOMAN FROM RICHARD RAMIREZ'S ATTACK?

A. An undercover police officer
B. A fire alarm
C. Her keys
D. A jammed gun

41. WHICH FACTS ARE TRUE ABOUT THE MONSTER OF FLORENCE?

A. He mailed body parts to a prosecutor
B. Some believe he is also the Zodiac Killer
C. Both A and B
D. A man was executed for the crimes but was later exonerated

42. WHAT DID POLICE FIND IN RANDY KRAFT'S CAR THAT LED TO HIS ARREST?

A. A map showing burial locations
B. A coded list believed to reference his victims

C. A diary detailing his crimes
D. A photo album of his victims

43. WHICH SERIAL KILLER DROVE A PURPLE HEARSE?

A. Rosemary West
B. Peter Sutcliffe
C. Lorenzo Gilyard
D. Pee Wee Gaskins

44. WHICH OF THESE STATEMENTS IS TRUE ABOUT SERIAL KILLER CARY STAYNER?

A. His younger brother was abducted and held captive for seven years
B. He requested child pornography in exchange for his confession
C. Police arrested him at a clothing-optional resort
D. All of the above

45. HOW DID SOUTH AFRICAN SERIAL KILLER DAISY DE MELKER COMMIT HER MURDERS?

A. Used poison to kill her spouses and son
B. Provided loans and then killed for insurance
C. Followed divine instructions to murder
D. Eliminated five men who wronged her

46. WHAT TOOL DID PETER SUTCLIFFE USE TO COMMIT HIS MURDERS?

A. A chainsaw
B. A ball-pein hammer
C. A knife
D. A garrote

47. WHAT ACTION MADE JACK THE RIPPER THE MOST NOTORIOUS SERIAL KILLER IN HISTORY?

A. His ability to evade capture
B. His use of poison

C. His manipulation of media
D. His public confessions

48. WHICH VICTIM OF THE BIRNIE MURDER SPREE WAS FOUND SITTING UP IN HER GRAVE?

A. Kate Moir
B. Denise Brown
C. Anne Marie
D. Charmaine Birnie

49. HOW DID KATE MOIR MANAGE TO ESCAPE FROM THE BIRNIES?

A. She overpowered David Birnie
B. She used a hidden weapon
C. She called the police from a grocery store
D. She fled into the wilderness

50. WHAT EARLY TRAUMA DID FRED WEST EXPERIENCE THAT CONTRIBUTED TO HIS DESCENT INTO SERIAL KILLING?

A. Witnessing a violent crime
B. Growing up in an incestuous household
C. Being abandoned by his parents
D. Suffering from a severe head injury

51. WHAT WAS THE PRIMARY METHOD USED BY IAN BRADY AND MYRA HINDLEY IN THE MOORS MURDERS?

A. Poisoning their victims
B. Strangulation and torture
C. Shooting from a distance
D. Setting victims on fire

52. WHAT CRIMINAL ACT MADE RAY AND FAYE COPELAND THE OLDEST COUPLE SENTENCED TO DEATH IN THE UNITED STATES?

A. They killed their own children
B. They murdered five drifters they hired

C. They orchestrated a bank heist
D. They were involved in human trafficking

53. HOW DID OTTIS TOOLE AND HENRY LEE LUCAS COLLABORATE IN THEIR SERIAL KILLING SPREE?

A. They formed a business partnership to commit crimes
B. They engaged in a sexual relationship while killing together
C. They operated independently without collaboration
D. They influenced each other to confess their crimes

54. WHAT HORRIFIC ACTION DID ROSEMARY WEST PERFORM ON HER STEPDAUGHTER CHARMAINE?

A. She poisoned her
B. She strangled her
C. She beat her until she refused to cry
D. She set her on fire

55. WHAT UNUSUAL FEATURE DID CLIVE PLAN TO INCLUDE WHEN REENACTING JACK THE RIPPER'S MURDERS?

A. Using a blood-soaked garment
B. Incorporating Masonic symbols
C. Leaving cryptic messages
D. Disguising himself as a medical professional

56. WHAT MOTIVE DID IAN BRADY HAVE FOR TAKING PICTURES DURING THE MOORS MURDERS?

A. To document his crimes for future reference
B. To blackmail the police
C. To create a photographic record of his dominance
D. To lure more victims

57. WHAT CRUCIAL MISTAKE LED TO THE CAPTURE OF IAN BRADY AND MYRA HINDLEY?

A. They confessed to all their crimes
B. A neighbor reported suspicious activities
C. Discovery of bodies in their garden
D. Surveillance footage caught them in the act

58. WHICH SERIAL KILLER DOES NOT FALL UNDER THE "ANGEL OF DEATH" CATEGORY?

A. Jane Toppan
B. Charles Cullen
C. Kristen Gilbert
D. Dorothea Puente

59. WHAT EVENT CONTRIBUTED TO THE ARREST OF NEXTPACKER SERIAL KILLER IVAN MILAT?

A. His wife provided a tip to authorities
B. A survivor identified Milat
C. Police noticed his car at a crime location
D. Milat's DNA matched evidence from a victim

60. TRUE OR FALSE: A FAMILY MEMBER OF IVAN MILAT ALSO COMMITTED MURDER IN BELANGLO STATE FOREST.

61. WHICH OF THE FOLLOWING WOMEN MANAGED TO ESCAPE FROM A SERIAL KILLER?

A. Tiffany Taylor
B. Carol DaRonch
C. Corazon Amurao
D. All of the above

62. HOW DID POLICE IDENTIFY NEW YORK SERIAL KILLER JOEL RIFKIN?

A. He emailed police, which was traced
B. A victim escaped and reported him
C. Police stopped him for a missing license plate and discovered a body
D. He was apprehended at one of his dumping sites

63. TRUE OR FALSE: JEFFREY DAHMER USED TO PHOTOBOMB HIS HIGH SCHOOL YEARBOOK'S NATIONAL HONOR SOCIETY PHOTO.

64. ACCORDING TO A DOCUMENTARY, WHICH TWO SERIAL KILLERS ENGAGED IN A ROMANTIC RELATIONSHIP WHILE IMPRISONED?

A. John Wayne Gacy and Pee Wee Gaskins
B. Myra Hindley and Rosemary West
C. Charles Ray Hatcher and Ottis Toole
D. Ian Brady and Fred West

65. WHICH OF THE FOLLOWING IS TRUE ABOUT BELGIAN SERIAL KILLER MARC DUTROUX?

A. His mother alerted police that he was detaining two girls
B. Two victims died while he was incarcerated
C. Two of his captives managed to escape
D. All of the above

66. WHAT WERE THE LAST WORDS OF AILEEN WUORNOS BEFORE HER EXECUTION?

A. "I'm leaving this world as I lived in it."
B. "I'm sailing with the Rock, and I'll be NEXT like 'Independence Day'"
C. "My actions were misunderstood."
D. "I repent for my sins."

67. WHICH OF THE FOLLOWING IS CORRECT ABOUT THE ROCHESTER ALPHABET MURDERS?

A. Authorities exhumed a suspect's remains for DNA analysis
B. The victims were discovered in towns beginning with the same letters as their names
C. A serial killer from California was linked to the crimes through DNA in 2011
D. BOTH A AND B

68. WHICH SERIAL KILLER WAS SUSPECTED IN THE ROCHESTER ALPHABET MURDERS BUT HAS REFUSED TO CONFESS?

A. Joseph James DeAngelo Jr.

B. Arthur Shawcross
C. Kenneth Bianchi
D. Richard Cottingham

69. WHAT IS KNOWN ABOUT THE CURRENT STATUS OF PEDRO ALONSO LÓPEZ, THE ANDES MONSTER?

A. He was executed in Peru
B. His current location and status are unknown
C. He was killed by an almost-victim
D. A victim's mother took justice into her own hands and killed him

70. WHICH OF THE FOLLOWING IS TRUE REGARDING THE SNOWTOWN MURDERS IN AUSTRALIA?

A. Four individuals participated in the killings
B. Eight victims were discovered inside barrels
C. There was an initiative to rename the town to Rosetown after the murders
D. ALL OF THE ABOVE

71. WHICH SERIAL KILLER WAS PERMITTED TO KEEP TWO PET PARAKEETS DURING HIS IMPRISONMENT?

A. Myra Hindley
B. Aileen Wuornos
C. Dennis Nilsen
D. Peter Dupas

72. TRUE OR FALSE: JOSEPH KALLINGER WAS ACCUSED OF KILLING HIS SON AND A NEIGHBOR AFTER CONFESSING IN HIS LIFE STORY BOOK.

73. HOW DID YOON YOUNG-CHUL, THE RAINCOAT KILLER, MANIPULATE HIS WAY OUT OF POLICE CUSTODY?

A. He feigned an epileptic attack
B. He leapt from a courtroom window
C. He slipped out of handcuffs using his raincoat sleeves
D. His girlfriend orchestrated a distraction at the station

74. WHAT DID YOON YOUNG-CHUL, THE RAINCOAT KILLER, USE TO MASK THE ODOR OF HIS VICTIMS' DECOMPOSED BODIES?

A. Drain cleaner
B. Kimchi
C. Bleach
D. Stink bombs

75. TRUE OR FALSE: AFTER COLLABORATING WITH TED BUNDY AT A CRISIS CENTER AND DISCOVERING HE WAS A SERIAL KILLER, ANN RULE DEVELOPED HER CAREER AS A CRIME WRITER.

76. WHAT WAS ED GEIN'S UNUSUAL SKILL THAT SURROUNDED HIS CRIMES?

A. Wood carving
B. Seamstressing with human skin
C. Metal forging
D. Glass blowing

77. WHICH FICTIONAL CHARACTERS WERE INSPIRED BY ED GEIN'S TERRIFYING ACTIONS?

A. Hannibal Lecter and Patrick Bateman
B. Leatherface, Norman Bates, and Buffalo Bill
C. Michael Myers and Freddy Krueger
D. Jason Voorhees and Pennywise

78. HOW DID CLIVE'S BIOGRAPHICAL APPROACH TO ED GEIN DIFFER FROM OTHER WRITERS?

A. He focused solely on Gein's crimes
B. He ignored Gein's personal life
C. He highlighted Gein's craftsmanship and personal traits
D. He wrote a fictionalized version of Gein's life

79. WHAT COMMON TRAITS DID CLIVE IDENTIFY AMONG SERIAL KILLERS IN HIS WRITINGS?

A. Financial instability and greed
B. Charismatic leadership and manipulation

C. Abusive childhoods and early warning signs
D. High intelligence and education

80. HOW DID CLIVE'S OWN LIFE REFLECT THE TRAITS HE STUDIED IN SERIAL KILLERS?

A. He had a stable and supportive family
B. He experienced abusive parents and exhibited early warning signs
C. He pursued a career in law enforcement
D. He had no personal connection to the subject matter

81. WHAT WAS THE NICKNAME GIVEN TO JOHN WAYNE GACY BY THE MEDIA?

A. The Night Clown
B. The Laughing Slayer
C. The Killer Clown
D. Pogo the Predator

82. WHAT METHOD DID CLIVE PLAN TO USE IF THE SPINNER SELECTED DENNIS NILSEN?

A. Poisoning his drink
B. Strangling after having sex
C. Setting him on fire
D. Stabbing with a knife

83. WHAT ROLE DID CLIVE'S BROTHER DEREK PLAY IN HIS WRITING PROCESS?

A. Derek assisted in research and writing
B. Derek tried to stop Clive from writing about serial killers
C. Derek demanded Clive attend his show instead of writing
D. Derek provided financial support for Clive's work

84. WHAT DISTURBING ARTIFACT DID CLIVE CREATE FOR HIS WORKSPACE?

A. A blood-stained knife
B. A chair upholstered in human skin
C. A lampshade made from a victim's face
D. A doll with stitched features

85. WHAT EVENT LEAD TO ED GEIN'S FINAL ARREST?

A. A routine police check
B. The disappearance of his last victim, Robert Piest
C. A public confrontation at a charity event
D. An anonymous tip to the authorities

86. HOW DID JOHN WAYNE GACY MANIPULATE HIS COMMUNITY TO LURE VICTIMS?

A. By offering free rides
B. By pretending to be a police officer
C. By performing as a clown and involving them in his act
D. By hosting large parties and inviting strangers

87. WHAT HORRIFYING BEHAVIOR DID TED BUNDY EXHIBIT TOWARDS HIS VICTIMS AFTER MURDERING THEM?

A. He left their bodies in public places
B. He revisited and engaged with their corpses
C. He set their houses on fire
D. He donated their remains to science

88. WHY DID DENNIS NILSEN GET CAUGHT BY POLICE?

A. He confessed to all his crimes
B. He left fingerprints at the crime scenes
C. A plumber found human remains in a drain
D. Surveillance footage caught him in the act

89. WHAT UNIQUE FEATURE DID CLIVE WANT TO INCLUDE WHEN MIMICKING JACK THE RIPPER'S MURDERS?

A. Using a blood-soaked garment
B. Integrating Masonic symbols
C. Leaving cryptic messages
D. Disguising himself as a medical professional

90. WHAT PERSONALITY TRAIT DID CLIVE FIND MOST AWESOME ABOUT THE 'KILLER CLOWN' NICKNAME?

A. Its alliteration
B. Its connection to popular culture
C. Its ability to disguise his true nature
D. Its unique and terrifying imagery

91. WHAT MADE KARLA HOMOLKA DECIDE TO HAND OVER HER SISTER TAMMY TO PAUL BERNARDO?

A. She was threatened with harm
B. She was promised money
C. She was turned on by Paul's actions
D. She wanted revenge

92. HOW DID MARTHA BECK AND RAYMOND FERNANDEZ MEET THEIR VICTIMS?

A. Through online dating profiles
B. Via lonely hearts ads
C. At local bars
D. Through mutual friends

93. WHAT CRITICAL EVIDENCE DID THE POLICE FIND THAT LINKED THE BIRNIES TO THEIR VICTIMS?

A. DNA samples
B. Surveillance footage
C. Video recordings of the crimes
D. Witness testimonies

94. WHAT HIDDEN MOTIVE DID CLIVE HAVE FOR USING THE THRILL-KILL WEBSITE?

A. To share his expertise on serial killers
B. To participate in virtual crime simulations
C. To plan real-life reenactments of serial killings
D. To gather information for a book

95. HOW DID THE POLICE EVENTUALLY UNCOVER THE BIRNIES' CRIMES?

A. Through forensic evidence
B. Via Kate Moir's escape and police report
C. By tracing financial transactions
D. Through anonymous tips

96. WHAT DICHOTOMY DID PSYCHIATRISTS DISCUSS REGARDING CATHERINE BIRNIE'S INVOLVEMENT IN THE CRIMES?

A. Loyalty vs. betrayal
B. Love vs. obsession
C. Power vs. weakness
D. Fear vs. courage

97. HOW DID ROSEMARY WEST'S CHILDHOOD CONTRIBUTE TO HER LIFE OF CRIME?

A. She was neglected by her parents
B. She witnessed domestic violence
C. She was raised in an incestuous household
D. She was bullied at school

98. WHAT FACTOR CONTRIBUTED TO THE FAILURE TO LINK KILLINGS TO ROSEMARY AND FRED WEST EARLIER?

A. Lack of forensic technology
B. Insufficient police resources
C. Victims were not reported missing
D. The couple's ability to manipulate and conceal evidence

99. WHAT WAS THE KEY PIECE OF EVIDENCE THAT LED TO THE CAPTURE OF IAN BRADY AND MYRA HINDLEY?

A. A confession by a co-conspirator
B. Discovery of their victims' remains on Saddleworth Moor
C. Surveillance footage of their crimes
D. A witness identifying them at the crime scene

100. WHAT MOTIVATION DID THE MOORS MURDERERS CLAIM FOR THEIR CRIMES DURING THEIR TRIAL?

A. Financial gain
B. Political ideology
C. Sexual gratification and control
D. Revenge against society

101. HOW DID THE MAKINS FINALLY BECOME SUSPECTS IN THE DISAPPEARANCES OF THE INFANTS?

A. A neighbor reported suspicious activities
B. A worker found infant bodies in a clogged drain
C. They were caught on surveillance cameras
D. A missing person report led to their arrest

102. WHAT WAS THE MOTIVE BEHIND DEBRA BROWN AND ALTON COLEMAN'S CRIMES?

A. Financial desperation
B. Thrill-seeking and dominance
C. Political beliefs
D. Revenge against their families

103. WHAT WERE GENDOLYN GRAHAM & CATHERINE MAY WOOD KNOWN FOR AFTER THEIR VICTIMS DIED?

A. They disposed of the bodies secretly
B. They bragged about their crimes
C. They hid the bodies in their cellar
D. They reported the deaths as accidents

104. WHAT WAS THE OUTCOME FOR CHARMAINE, THE STEPDAUGHTER OF FRED AND ROSEMARY WEST?

A. She survived and testified against them
B. She escaped and fled the country
C. She disappeared and was never found
D. She was found alive years later

105. WHAT ROLE DID CATHERINE BIRNIE PLAY IN THE BIRNIE MURDER SPREE?

A. She was the mastermind behind the crimes
B. She was an unwilling accomplice
C. She actively participated in the rapes and murders
D. She only provided logistical support

106. HOW DID FRED WEST AND ROSEMARY WEST ENSURE THEIR VICTIMS WERE DEAD BEFORE DISPOSING OF THEM?

A. By using poison
B. By strangulation
C. By repeatedly shooting their victims
D. By using a combination of strangulation and bludgeoning

107. WHAT EVENT LED TO THE FINAL CAPTURE OF THE MOORS MURDERERS?

A. A routine traffic stop
B. A neighbor witnessing suspicious behavior
C. A failed attempt to involve Myra's younger brother
D. A confession by a co-conspirator

108. WHAT WAS THE MAIN REASON FOR DEBRA BROWN'S LIFE SENTENCE DESPITE HER PARTICIPATION IN CRIMES WITH ALTON COLEMAN?

A. Lack of physical evidence
B. Her low IQ and dependent personality
C. Her cooperation with the police
D. Her claim of innocence

109. HOW DID GEORGE AND CHARLENE GALLEGO DIFFER IN THEIR INVOLVEMENT IN THEIR CRIMES?

A. Gerald was the primary perpetrator while Charlene was an accomplice
B. Charlene led the murders while Gerald handled logistics
C. Both were equally involved in the rapes and murders
D. Only Gerald committed the murders while Charlene was unaware

110. WHAT WAS THE REAL NAME OF THE SISTER TRIO KNOWN AS LAS POQUIANCHIS?

A. Maria, Elena, Sofia, and Rosa
B. Delfina, Maria, Carmen, and Luisa
C. Isabel, Patricia, Laura, and Teresa
D. Ana, Beatriz, Claudia, and Monica

111. WHO WAS CONVICTED AS THE FIRST KNOWN SERIAL KILLER IN BRITAIN?

A. Amelia Dyer
B. Mary Ann Cotton
C. Felícitas Sánchez
D. Hélène Jégado

112. WHICH EMPRESS HAD TO INTERVENE TO ARREST DARYA NIKOLAYEVNA SALTYKOVA FOR HER CRIMES?

A. Empress Maria Theresa
B. Empress Elizabeth
C. Empress Catherine II
D. Empress Anna

113. HOW MANY BABIES IS AMELIA DYER BELIEVED TO HAVE KILLED?

A. Over 100
B. More than 400
C. Approximately 50
D. About 200

114. WHAT CRIME DID MARIA CATHERINA SWANENBURG USE TO KILL HER VICTIMS?

A. Strangulation
B. Poisoning with arsenic
C. Shooting
D. Bludgeoning

115. HOW DID HELENE JEGADO'S SERIAL KILLING SPREE COME TO AN END?

A. She confessed to all her crimes
B. A detective linked her to multiple deaths through autopsies
C. She was caught red-handed committing a murder
D. She died before she could be arrested

116. HOW MANY MURDERS IS GENENE ANNE JONES BELIEVED TO HAVE COMMITTED?

A. Between 5 and 10
B. Anywhere from eleven to forty-six
C. Approximately twenty
D. Over fifty

117. WHAT MOTIVE DID FELÍCITAS SÁNCHEZ HAVE FOR KILLING CHILDREN?

A. Financial gain
B. Revenge against society
C. Hatred for children stemming from her own neglected childhood
D. Political ideology

118. WHO WERE THE SERIAL KILLER COUPLE RESPONSIBLE FOR THE MOORS MURDERS?

A. Fred and Rosemary West
B. Ray and Faye Copeland
C. Ian Brady and Myra Hindley
D. Dennis Rader and his accomplice

119. WHAT HORRIFIC ACTION DID GERALD AND CHARLENE GALLEGO TAKE WITH THEIR VICTIMS AFTER RAPING THEM?

A. They left their victims in public places
B. They mutilated and dismembered their bodies
C. They kept their victims as sex slaves before murdering them
D. They set their victims on fire

120. WHAT DID JOACHIM KROLL DO TO HIS VICTIMS AFTER MURDERING THEM?

A. Buried them in his backyard
B. Burned their bodies
C. Ate parts of their bodies
D. Left them in public places

121. HOW DID JOACHIM KROLL GET CAUGHT BY THE POLICE?

A. He confessed during interrogation
B. A neighbor reported a clogged toilet
C. Surveillance footage captured him
D. He was recognized by a victim's family

122. WHY DID ANDREI CHIKATALO PREFER STABBING HIS WOMEN?

A. It was quicker than other methods
B. It allowed him to control the moment of death
C. He believed it gave him an orgasm
D. It was easier to dispose of the bodies

123. HOW DID ANDREI CHIKATALO COME TO TERMS WITH HIS MURDERS?

A. He expressed deep remorse
B. He justified his actions as necessary
C. He saw them as the only way to satisfy his urges
D. He blamed society for his behavior

124. WHICH SERIAL KILLER APPEARED AND WON ON "THE DATING GAME"?

A. Ted Bundy
B. Rodney Alcala
C. Jeffrey Dahmer
D. Dennis Rader

125. HOW DID RODNEY ALCALA ESCAPE CAPTURE AFTER HIS FIRST MURDER?

A. He bribed the police
B. He used a hidden weapon
C. He escaped during a police visit
D. He hid in a remote location

126. WHAT LED TO THE FINAL CAPTURE OF DEAN CORLL, THE "DISCO DADDY"?

A. A witness saw him commit a murder
B. He was recognized on television
C. His accomplice shot him and called the police
D. He left DNA evidence at the crime scene

127. WHO WERE THE MOORS MURDERERS AND WHAT MADE THEIR CRIMES NOTABLE?

A. Fred and Rosemary West, known for their extreme violence
B. Ian Brady and Myra Hindley, known for burying victims on Saddleworth Moor
C. Ray and Faye Copeland, known as the oldest death-sentenced couple
D. Ottis Elwood Toole and Henry Lee Lucas, known for their numerous confessions

128. WHAT HAPPENED TO RAY AND FAYE COPELAND BEFORE THEIR DEATH SENTENCES WERE CARRIED OUT?

A. They escaped from prison
B. They were exonerated
C. They died in prison
D. Their sentences were commuted

129. WHAT DID GERARD AND CHARLENE GALLEGO DO TO THEIR VICTIMS?

A. They poisoned them
B. They kept them as sex slaves before murdering them
C. They abducted and left them to die
D. They used them for human experiments

130. WHAT DISTURBING ACT DID JOACHIM KROLL PERFORM ON HIS VICTIMS AFTER KILLING THEM?

A. Burned their bodies in open flames
B. Dissected and consumed their flesh
C. Left them in public parks
D. Bury them in deep graves

131. HOW DID JOACHIM KROLL EVENTUALLY GET CAUGHT BY THE POLICE?

A. He voluntarily confessed to all his crimes
B. A neighbor noticed a foul smell and reported it
C. A plumber discovered human remains in a drain
D. Surveillance footage captured him committing a murder

132. WHAT MOTIVE DID ANDREI CHIKATALO CLAIM FOR STABBING HIS VICTIMS?

A. Revenge against society
B. Achieving an orgasm
C. Collecting trophies
D. Eliminating perceived enemies

133. HOW MANY MURDERS DID ANDREI CHIKATALO CONFESS TO BEFORE HIS EXECUTION?

A. 25
B. 35
C. 50
D. 56

134. WHICH TELEVISION SHOW DID SERIAL KILLER RODNEY ALCALA PARTICIPATE IN AND WIN A DATE?

A. The Bachelor
B. Survivor
C. The Dating Game
D. Big Brother

135. WHAT EVENT LED TO DEAN CORLL'S CAPTURE WHILE COMMITTING A CRIME?

A. He was caught on surveillance footage
B. An accomplice turned himself in and shot Corll
C. He accidentally left evidence at the crime scene
D. A victim managed to escape and alert the authorities

136. WHAT SECRET LIFE DID GILLES DE RAIS LEAD ALONGSIDE JOAN OF ARC?

A. He was a renowned musician secretly funding his crimes
B. He was a soldier who also tortured and murdered children
C. He was an undercover spy manipulating political figures
D. He was a wealthy merchant laundering money through his business

137. WHAT TITLE DID PEDRO LOPEZ EARN DUE TO HIS EXTENSIVE MURDERS IN SOUTHERN AMERICA?

A. The Andean Shadow
B. The Monster of the Andes
C. The South American Slayer
D. The Jungle Butcher

138. WHAT HORRIFIC ACTION DID ALBERT FISH CLAIM TO HAVE PERFORMED ON HIS VICTIM, GRACE BUDD?

A. He set her ablaze
B. He strangled and dismembered her
C. He left her in a frozen wasteland
D. He suffocated her with a pillow

139. WHAT UNIQUE FEATURE DID ALBERT FISH USE TO TAUNT THE MOTHER OF ONE OF HIS VICTIMS?

A. He sent her photographs of his crimes
B. He sent her a detailed letter describing his murders
C. He sent her pieces of his victims as souvenirs
D. He followed her to her home and threatened her

140. WHO WAS CONSIDERED THE WORST SERIAL KILLER IN IRAN, RESPONSIBLE FOR THE DEATH OF SIXTEEN WOMEN?

A. Vahid Afshar
B. Said Hanai
C. Reza Pahlavi
D. Amir Hossein

141. WHAT MADE ISRAEL KEYES A UNIQUE SERIAL KILLER IN TERMS OF HIS MURDER PLANNING?

A. He targeted only family members
B. He killed in the same location repeatedly
C. He had no specific victim profile and killed far from his usual haunts
D. He used only firearms for his murders

142. WHICH SERIAL KILLER WAS KNOWN AS THE "SCORE CARD KILLER" AND TARGETED MARINES?

A. Dennis Rader
B. Randy Kraft
C. Ted Bundy
D. Gary Ridgway

143. HOW WERE CHARLES CHI-TAT NG AND LEONARD LAKE CAPTURED FOR THEIR SERIAL KILLINGS?

A. They were caught in the act of a murder
B. Charles was arrested for shoplifting, leading to the discovery of their crimes
C. They confessed voluntarily to their murders
D. A hidden camera recorded their crimes

144. WHAT PARALYZING DRUG DID "ANGEL OF DEATH" VICKIE DAWN JACKSON USE TO KILL HER VICTIMS?

A. Strychnine
B. Mivacron
C. Cyanide
D. Arsenic

145. WHAT WERE THE FIRST WORDS OF DAVID RICHARD BERKOVITZ, THE SON OF SAM, WHEN HE WAS ARRESTED?

A. "I regret nothing."
B. "What took you so long?"
C. "I was just hungry."
D. "You'll never catch me."

146. WHAT CRUCIAL MISTAKE DID THE BIRNIES MAKE THAT LED TO THE CAPTURE OF DAVID BIRNIE?

A. Leaving fingerprints at the crime scene
B. Using a distinctive weapon
C. Being overconfident and making a brutal error
D. Confessing to the murders

147. WHAT MOTIVATION DID PSYCHIATRISTS SUGGEST FOR CATHERINE BIRNIE'S PARTICIPATION IN THE MURDERS?

A. Financial gain
B. Obsession and loyalty to David
C. Mental illness
D. Revenge against society

148. HOW DID FRED WEST AND ROSEMARY WEST'S CHILDHOOD EXPERIENCES CONTRIBUTE TO THEIR CRIMINAL BEHAVIOR?

A. They were both neglected and starved
B. They grew up in violent, incestuous households
C. They were isolated from society
D. They were forced into early marriages

149. WHAT METHOD DID "ANGEL OF DEATH" VICKIE DAWN JACKSON USE TO ENSURE HER VICTIMS COULD NOT ESCAPE?

A. Strangulation
B. Injection of a paralyzing drug
C. Use of handcuffs
D. Setting up traps in the room

150. WHO IS CONSIDERED THE MOST PROLIFIC SERIAL KILLER IN CONNECTICUT?

A. Dennis Rader
B. William Devin Howell
C. Ted Bundy
D. Jeffrey Dahmer

151. WHAT EVENT INITIATED THE SEARCH FOR THE LONG ISLAND SERIAL KILLER?

A. The disappearance of Shannan Gilbert
B. The discovery of Melissa Barthelemy's body
C. The abduction of Valerie Mack
D. The murder of Jessica Taylor

152. WHAT UNIQUE BEHAVIOR DID THE DOODLER SERIAL KILLER EXHIBIT BEFORE MURDERING HIS VICTIMS?

A. Leaving cryptic notes
B. Sketching his victims
C. Sending taunting messages to the police
D. Using disguises during the attacks

153. IN WHICH CITY WERE THE TORSO MURDERS COMMISSIONED BY THE CLEVELAND TORSO KILLER?

A. Chicago, Illinois
B. Cleveland, Ohio
C. New York, New York
D. Dallas, Texas

154. WHAT DISTINGUISHED THE COLONIAL PARKWAY KILLER FROM OTHER SERIAL KILLERS?

A. Targeting only single individuals
B. Killing victims in pairs within their cars
C. Using poison as the primary method
D. Leaving behind symbolic clues

155. WHAT MOTIVATION DID DR. MICHAEL SWANGO CLAIM FOR HIS SERIAL KILLINGS?

A. Financial gain
B. Thrill-seeking and obsession with death
C. Revenge against society
D. Religious fanaticism

156. WHAT CRIMINAL ACT DID THE SERVANT GIRL KILLER USE TO MURDER HIS VICTIMS?

A. Poisoning
B. Shooting
C. Stabbing with an ax
D. Strangulation

157. HOW DID THE COLUMBIA PARKWAY KILLER HANDLE HIS VICTIMS' VEHICLES POST-MURDER?

A. Left them at the crime scene
B. Disposed of them in rivers
C. Drove them away from the location
D. Destroyed them with fire

158. WHAT UNIQUE CRIMINAL NAME DID HENRY LEE LUCAS AND OTTIS ELWOOD TOOLE SHARE?

A. The Twin Torso Killers
B. The Devil's Duo
C. The Death Partners
D. The Serial Killer Couple

159. HOW DID GERALD AND CHARLENE GALLEGO SELECT THEIR VICTIMS?

A. Randomly encountered individuals on the street
B. Teenage girls they lured into their van for work
C. Specific targets from a prepared list
D. Victims from online advertisements

160. WHICH SERIAL KILLER DUO RECORDED THEIR VICTIMS' SCREAMS DURING THEIR CRIMES?

A. Ian Brady and Myra Hindley
B. Lawrence Bittaker and Roy Norris
C. Fred and Rosemary West
D. Kenneth Bianchi and Angelo Buono

161. HOW DID THE HARPER BROTHERS DISPOSE OF THEIR VICTIMS?

A. Buried them in their backyard
B. Threw them into rivers
C. Filled their chest cavities with rocks and placed them in the river
D. Burned their bodies in secluded areas

162. WHAT WAS THE NAME OF THE VAN USED BY LAWRENCE BITTAKER AND ROY NORRIS IN THEIR SERIAL KILLING SPREE?

A. Death Wagon
B. The Bloodmobile
C. Murder Mack
D. The Screaming Stallion

163. WHAT MOTIVATED WILLIAM HARPER AND HIS BROTHER TO KILL MORE PEOPLE FOR SPORT THAN FOR MONEY?

A. Financial gain
B. A desire for power and control
C. Competition with other criminals
D. Thrill-seeking and enjoyment of the act

164. HOW DID THE HILLSIDE STRANGLERS LURE THEIR VICTIMS INTO THEIR VEHICLE?

A. Offering them a ride home
B. Pretending to be undercover police officers
C. Advertising fake job opportunities
D. Using charms and sweet talk

165. WHAT ACTION BY STEVEN GORDON CONTRIBUTED TO HIS LIFE SENTENCE FOR SERIAL KILLING?

A. Attempting to escape prison
B. Confessing to all his crimes
C. Showing remorse in court
D. Wearing ankle monitors while on probation

166. WHAT HORRIFIC ACT DID ROSEMARY WEST PERFORM ON HER STEPDAUGHTER CHARMAINE?

A. Poisoned her
B. Strangled her
C. Beat her until she refused to cry
D. Set her on fire

167. WHAT UNUSUAL FEATURE DID CLIVE PLAN TO INCLUDE WHEN REENACTING JACK THE RIPPER'S MURDERS?

A. Using a blood-soaked garment
B. Incorporating Masonic symbols
C. Leaving cryptic messages
D. Disguising himself as a medical professional

168. WHAT CRIMINAL ACT MADE RAY AND FAYE COPELAND THE OLDEST COUPLE SENTENCED TO DEATH IN THE UNITED STATES?

A. They killed their own children
B. They murdered five drifters they hired
C. They orchestrated a bank heist
D. They were involved in human trafficking

169. WHAT MOTIVATED OTTIS TOOLE AND HENRY LEE LUCAS TO KILL TOGETHER?

A. Financial gain
B. A shared ideological belief
C. A sexual relationship and mutual influence
D. Revenge against society

170. WHAT HORRIFIC METHOD DID GERALD AND CHARLENE GALLEGO USE TO KILL THEIR VICTIMS?

A. They used a firearm to shoot
B. They strangled their victims in public places
C. They kept victims as sex slaves before murdering them
D. They poisoned their victims' food

171. WHAT LEGAL ACTION LED TO THE CAPTURE OF IAN BRADY AND MYRA HINDLEY?

A. They confessed to their crimes
B. A neighbor reported suspicious activities
C. Discovery of bodies in their garden
D. Surveillance footage caught them in the act

172. WHAT SINISTER TRAIT DID CLIVE ADMIRE IN JOHN WAYNE GACY'S NICKNAME?

A. Its alliteration
B. Its connection to popular culture
C. Its unique and terrifying imagery
D. Its simplicity and brevity

173. HOW DID STEVEN GORDON AND FRANC CANO'S SERIAL KILLINGS COME to an end?

A. They were both killed by their victims
B. They were caught due to faulty ankle monitors
C. They escaped and were never found
D. They turned themselves in voluntarily

174. WHAT MAKES THE FINCHLEY BABY FARMERS' CRIMES PARTICULARLY HORRIFIC?

A. They used a unique weapon
B. They targeted only newborns
C. They killed babies they were supposed to care for
D. They dismembered their victims

175. WHAT CRIMINAL ACT DID WILLY HARPER AND HIS BROTHER COMMIT THAT SHOCKED RIVER PIRATES?

A. They robbed and murdered ships
B. They lured travelers to bluffs and shoved them off
C. They sabotaged boats and caused drownings
D. They engaged in piracy and slave trading

176. HOW DID LAWRENCE BITTAKER AND ROY NORRIS TEST THEIR SERIAL KILLING PLAN BEFORE ACTING?

A. They conducted surveillance on potential victims
B. They performed a test run by picking up local girls and taking their pictures
C. They simulated the crimes in their van
D. They consulted with other criminals for advice

177. WHAT EVENT CAUSED THE HARPER BROTHERS TO BE CAUGHT?

A. A neighbor reported suspicious activities
B. They were seen committing a murder
C. Moses Stegall attacked Big Harper
D. They confessed to their crimes

178. WHAT LEGAL ACTION ENSURED THAT ROSEMARY WEST WOULD NEVER BE RELEASED FROM PRISON?

A. She was given multiple life sentences
B. She was granted permanent parole denial
C. She was given papers stating she would never get out
D. She was declared insane and institutionalized

179. WHAT CRIMINAL ACT DID WILLY HARPER AND HIS BROTHER PERFORM THAT INCENSED EVERYONE THEY MET?

A. They robbed local businesses
B. They killed travelers and lured them to bluffs
C. They vandalized properties and buildings
D. They committed acts of public indecency

180. WHICH TWO SISTER SERIAL KILLERS WERE THE FIRST WOMEN EXECUTED IN MODERN EGYPT?

A. Agatha and Tabitha
B. Rosemary and Fred West
C. Raya and Sakina
D. Cyndi and Charlene Gallego

181. HOW DID DENISE BROWN SURVIVE HER INITIAL BURIAL BY THE BIRNIE BROTHERS?

A. She escaped through a hidden door
B. She screamed loudly for help
C. She sat up in her grave
D. She was rescued by a passerby

182. WHAT EVENT LED TO THE CAPTURE OF JOHN DUFFY AND DAVID MULCAHY, THE RAILWAY KILLERS?

A. DNA evidence linked them to the crimes
B. A witness saw them commit a murder
C. John Duffy confessed after ten years
D. They were caught in the act of killing

183. FOR HOW MANY YEARS DID LOREN HERZOG AND WESLEY SHERMANTINE, KNOWN AS THE SPEED FREAK KILLERS, CONTINUE THEIR MURDER SPREE?

A. 5 years
B. 10 years
C. 15 years
D. 20 years

184. WHAT METHOD DID FRED WEST USE TO ABUSE HIS STEPDAUGHTER CHARMAINE?

A. Poisoning her
B. Strangulation
C. Beating her until she refused to cry
D. Setting her on fire

185. WHICH SERIAL KILLER COUPLE WERE RESPONSIBLE FOR THE MOORS MURDERS IN THE UNITED KINGDOM?

A. John and Mary Pizzarelli
B. Ian Brady and Myra Hindley
C. Raymond Fernandez and Martha Beck
D. Ronald and James Allridge

186. WHAT CRIMINAL ACT MADE RAY AND FAYE COPELAND THE OLDEST COUPLE SENTENCED TO DEATH IN THE UNITED STATES?

A. They killed their own children
B. They murdered five drifters they hired
C. They orchestrated a bank heist
D. They were involved in human trafficking

187. HOW DID OTTIS ELWOOD TOOLE AND HENRY LEE LUCAS COLLABORATE IN THEIR SERIAL KILLING SPREE?

A. They formed a business partnership to commit crimes
B. They engaged in a sexual relationship while killing together
C. They operated independently without collaboration
D. They influenced each other to confess their crimes

188. WHAT HORRIFIC ACTION DID ROSEMARY WEST PERFORM ON HER STEPDAUGHTER CHARMAINE?

A. She poisoned her
B. She strangled her
C. She beat her until she refused to cry
D. She set her on fire

189. WHAT WERE CARL PANZRAM'S LAST WORDS BEFORE HIS EXECUTION?

A. "I have nothing to say."
B. "I'm ready to go."
C. "Hurry it up, you Hoosier bastard! I could hang a dozen men while you're screwing around!"
D. "Take your time. Don't bungle it."

190. WHICH SERIAL KILLER QUESTIONED IF THEY COULD HEAR THEIR OWN BLOOD AFTER BEING EXECUTED?

A. John Wayne Gacy
B. Ted Bundy
C. Peter Kürten
D. Jeffrey Dahmer

191. WHICH SERIAL KILLER REMAINED SILENT DURING THEIR EXECUTION?

A. Amelia Dyer
B. Ray Copeland
C. Fred West
D. Dennis Nilsen

192. WHAT WERE PETER MANUEL'S LAST WORDS BEFORE HIS DEATH?

A. "I'm ready to go."
B. "Turn up the radio and I'll go quietly."
C. "I forgive you all."
D. "Take care of my family."

193. WHAT MESSAGE DID TED BUNDY WANT TO CONVEY WITH HIS LAST WORDS?

A. "I have nothing to say."
B. "Kiss my ass."
C. "I'd like you to give my love to my family and friends."
D. "Take your time. Don't bungle it."

194. WHAT UNHOLY FAREWELL DID JOHN WAYNE GACY EXPRESS BEFORE HIS EXECUTION?

A. "I repent, but I do not fear death."
B. "I don't care if I live or die."
C. "Kiss my ass."
D. "I'm sailing with the rock."

195. WHAT WERE JEFFREY DAHMER'S FINAL WORDS BEFORE HIS EXECUTION?

A. "I have nothing to say."
B. "I don't care if I live or die. Go ahead and kill me."
C. "Take care of my family."
D. "I forgive you all."

196. WHAT FINAL ADVICE DID WILLIAM BONIN OFFER BEFORE HIS EXECUTION?

A. "I have nothing to say."
B. "I would suggest that when a person has a thought of doing anything serious against the law, that before they did that they should go to a quiet place and think about it seriously."
C. "Take your time. Don't bungle it."
D. "I'm ready to go."

197. WHAT LAMENTABLE STATEMENT DID ALBERT FISH MAKE BEFORE HIS DEATH?

A. "I forgive you all."
B. "I have nothing to say."
C. "I don't even know why I'm here."
D. "I repent, but I do not fear death."

198. WHAT FAREWELL DID ANGEL MATURINO RESENDIZ EXPRESS BEFORE HIS EXECUTION?

A. "I'm sailing with the rock."
B. "I don't care if I live or die."
C. "I want to ask if it is in your heart to forgive me."
D. "I'm ready to go."

199. WHAT LAST WORDS DID FRITZ HAARMANN EXPRESS REGARDING DEATH?

A. "I don't care if I live or die."
B. "I repent, but I do not fear death."
C. "Take your time. Don't bungle it."
D. "I'm ready to go."

200. WHAT INSIGHTFUL STATEMENT DID DONALD HENRY GASKINS MAKE BEFORE HIS EXECUTION?

A. "I have nothing to say."
B. "I forgive you all."
C. "I don't even know why I'm here."
D. "I'll let my lawyers talk for me. I'm ready to go."

201. WHAT FAREWELL DID RAYMOND FERNANDEZ OFFER BEFORE HIS EXECUTION?

A. “I have nothing to say.”
B. “I want to shout it out, I love Martha! What do the public know about love?”
C. “I forgive you all.”
D. “Take care of my family.”

202. WHAT MORBID SUGGESTION DID MARTHA BECK MAKE IN HER FINAL WORDS?

A. “I have nothing to say.”
B. “My story is a love story. But only those tortured by love can know what I mean... Imprisonment in the Death House has only strengthened my feelings for Raymond...”
C. “I’m ready to go.”
D. “I forgive you all.”

203. WHAT SIMPLE FAREWELL DID EARLE NELSON OFFER BEFORE HIS EXECUTION?

A. “I have nothing to say.”
B. “I’m sailing with the rock.”
C. “I’m going home, babe.”
D. “Take care of my family.”

204. WHAT FINAL WORDS DID ANGEL MATURINO RESENDIZ EXPRESS REGARDING FORGIVENESS?

A. “I forgive you all.”
B. “I’m ready to go.”
C. “I want to ask if it is in your heart to forgive me. You don't have to. I know I allowed the devil to rule my life. I just ask you to forgive me and ask the Lord to forgive me for allowing the devil to deceive me. I thank God for having patience in me. You did not deserve this. I deserve what I am getting.”
D. “Take care of my family.”

205. WHAT APOLOGETIC STATEMENT DID FRITZ HAARMANN MAKE BEFORE HIS EXECUTION?

A. "I have nothing to say."
B. "I repent, but I do not fear death."
C. "I forgive you all."
D. "I'm ready to go."

206. WHAT LAST WORDS DID DONALD HENRY GASKINS EXPRESS REGARDING HIS LEGAL REPRESENTATION?

A. "I have nothing to say."
B. "I forgive you all."
C. "I don't care if I live or die."
D. "I'll let my lawyers talk for me. I'm ready to go."

207. WHAT DEVIOUS PLANNING DID MARCEL PETIOT INCORPORATE INTO HIS FINAL WORDS?

A. He left a cryptic message
B. He warned the authorities
C. He issued a final threat
D. He advised witnesses to look away

208. WHAT WARNING DID FRANCIS CROWELY GIVE BEFORE HIS EXECUTION?

A. "I have nothing to say."
B. "Look away. This will not be pretty to see."
C. "I forgive you all."
D. "Take care of my family."

209. WHAT PLEA FOR FORGIVENESS DID HEATHER WEST EXPRESS BEFORE HER DEATH?

A. "I have nothing to say."
B. "I forgive you all."
C. [Heather West did not have recorded last words]
D. "I'm ready to go."

210. WHAT FINAL STATEMENT DID FRANK HUNTER MAKE BEFORE HIS EXECUTION?

A. “I repent, but I do not fear death.”
B. “I don’t even know why I’m here.”
C. “I forgive you all.”
D. “I’m ready to go.”

211. WHAT TRAGIC EVENT DID HEATHER WEST FACE AFTER BEING ABUSED BY HER PARENTS?

A. She escaped and lived freely
B. She testified against her parents
C. She disappeared without a trace
D. She was rescued by neighbors

212. WHAT DID FRIEDMAN HAARMANN EXPRESS REGARDING HIS FUTURE AFTER REPENTANCE?

A. “I forgive you all.”
B. “I have nothing to say.”
C. “I repent, but I do not fear death.”
D. “I’m ready to go.”

213. WHAT LAST WORDS DID ALBERT FISH EXPRESS BEFORE HIS EXECUTION?

A. “I forgive you all.”
B. “I’m ready to go.”
C. “I don’t even know why I’m here.”
D. “Take care of my family.”

214. WHAT APOLOGETIC STATEMENT DID ANGEL RESENDIZ MAKE BEFORE HIS DEATH?

A. “I have nothing to say.”
B. “I forgive you all.”
C. “I want to ask if it is in your heart to forgive me. You don't have to. I know I allowed the devil to rule my life. I just ask you to forgive me and ask the Lord to forgive me for allowing the devil to deceive me. I thank God for having patience in me. You did not deserve this. I deserve what I am getting.”
D. “I’m ready to go.”

215. WHAT INFAMOUS NICKNAME WAS GIVEN TO ELIZABETH SHORT IN HER UNSOLVED MURDER CASE?

A. The Black Widow
B. The Black Dahlia
C. The Crimson Claw
D. The Silent Shadow

216. HOW OLD WAS JONBENET RAMSEY WHEN SHE WAS FOUND DEAD IN HER HOME?

A. Five years old
B. Six years old
C. Seven years old
D. Eight years old

217. WHAT MADE THE ISDAL WOMAN CASE IN NORWAY SO MYSTERIOUS?

A. Her body was found in a lake untouched
B. Her belongings were meticulously burned
C. She was killed by a wild animal
D. She left a detailed diary explaining her death

218. WHAT UNIQUE REQUEST DID THE AXEMAN OF NEW ORLEANS MAKE TO THE PUBLIC TO AVOID BEING TARGETED?

A. Play classical music at home
B. Listen to jazz music
C. Light candles in the windows
D. Keep doors locked at all times

219. WHO WAS CONVICTED IN CONNECTION TO THE 1982 TYLENOL MURDERS?

A. James Lewis
B. Ted Bundy
C. John Wayne Gacy
D. Dennis Rader

220. WHY WAS THE AMBER ALERT SYSTEM ESTABLISHED?

A. To locate missing pets
B. To notify about dangerous weather
C. To assist in the immediate search for abducted children
D. To provide updates during natural disasters

221. WHAT SET THE ZODIAC KILLER APART FROM OTHER SERIAL KILLERS IN HISTORY?

A. He used a unique weapon in every murder
B. He sent cryptic letters and ciphers to newspapers
C. He only targeted high-profile individuals
D. He operated exclusively in one city

222. WHAT CRUCIAL INVESTIGATION ERROR DID POLICE MAKE IN THE JONBENET RAMSEY CASE?

A. Ignoring the ransom note's demands
B. Focusing solely on external suspects
C. Sealing only her bedroom instead of the entire house
D. Allowing friends and family to mingle with the crime scene

223. WHAT FINAL ACTION DID JAMES LEWIS CLAIM TO HELP SOLVE THE TYLENOL MURDERS AFTER HIS CONVICTION?

A. He provided a full confession to the murders
B. He described the killer's appearance
C. He sketched how the killer tampered with the bottles
D. He revealed the location of the remaining victims

224. WHAT MADE THE GATTON MURDERS CASE SO STRANGE AND CONFUSING IN AUSTRALIA'S HISTORY?

A. The victims were all related
B. The murders happened in broad daylight
C. The motive and perpetrator remain unknown
D. The crime scene was meticulously preserved

225. WHAT UNIQUE FACT LINKED FRANCIS TUMBLETY TO THE RAHWAY JANE DOE MURDER CASE?

A. He was found at the crime scene
B. He had a personal vendetta against her
C. He lived thirty-five minutes away from where her body was found
D. He confessed to the murder

226. WHAT INSPIRED EDGAR ALLAN POE TO WRITE "THE MYSTERY OF MARIE ROGET"?

A. The Gatton murders
B. The Rahway Jane Doe case
C. The Mary Rogers murder
D. The Moors Murders

227. WHAT WAS THE PRIMARY REASON THE HALL-MILLS MURDERS REMAIN UNSOLVED?

A. Lack of eyewitnesses
B. Contamination of evidence by onlookers
C. The couple had solid alibis
D. Advanced forensic techniques were not available

228. HOW DID BETTY SHANKS' MURDER CASE IN 1952 STAND OUT AMONG UNSOLVED CASES IN AUSTRALIA?

A. It was the first case to use DNA evidence
B. The victim was a well-known public figure
C. It involved a suspected sex offender but no arrests were made
D. The crime scene was perfectly preserved

229. WHAT DISTINGUISHED THE OLD MURDER CASES BEFORE THE 1900s IN TERMS OF EVIDENCE HANDLING?

A. They used advanced forensic techniques
B. Crime scenes were strictly protected by law
C. Onlookers often trampled and took souvenirs from crime scenes
D. Police arrived immediately to secure the area

230. WHAT ROLE DID CATHERINE WEST PLAY IN THE CRIMES COMMITTED WITH HER HUSBAND FRED WEST?

A. She actively participated in the rapes
B. She was unaware of the murders
C. She acted as a lookout during the crimes
D. She only provided financial support

231. WHAT MADE THE DISAPPEARANCE OF THE SPRINGFIELD THREE EXTRAORDINARILY HAUNTING?

A. Their belongings were scattered around the neighborhood
B. There were signs of a violent struggle
C. All their possessions, including cars, were left untouched
D. They left behind cryptic messages

232. WHEN WAS JODI HUISENTRIUT LEGALLY DECLARED DEAD AFTER HER DISAPPEARANCE?

A. 1995
B. 1997
C. 2001
D. 2004

233. WHAT CLUE WAS FOUND NEAR THE LOCATION WHERE ASHA DEGREE LAST WAS SEEN?

A. A torn piece of clothing
B. Candy wrappers and a pencil
C. A discarded phone
D. A threatening note

234. WHAT ACTION DID AMY WROE BETCHEL'S HUSBAND TAKE THAT RAISED SUSPECTS ABOUT HER DISAPPEARANCE?

A. He provided a solid alibi
B. He destroyed evidence
C. His journals depicted violence towards women
D. He confessed to the crime

235. WHAT MADE THE SODDER CHILDREN'S DISAPPEARANCE ONE OF THE MOST MYSTERIOUS CASES IN HISTORY?

A. Their disappearance occurred during a tornado
B. Only four out of ten children were accounted for
C. Their family moved to another country
D. They left behind detailed clues

236. WHAT EVIDENCE LINKED STEVE BETCHEL TO HIS WIFE AMY'S DISAPPEARANCE?

A. Fingerprints on her belongings
B. Surveillance footage of the abduction
C. Violent imagery in his journals
D. A confession to a friend

237. HOW DID TARA CALICO'S DISAPPEARANCE BECOME CONNECTED TO A POLAROID PICTURE FOUND YEARS LATER?

A. The picture showed her at the scene of her disappearance
B. The woman in the picture resembled Tara and had a matching scar
C. The picture contained a map leading to her location
D. The Polaroid included a confession note

238. WHAT WAS THE FINAL TRUTH REVEALED ABOUT BOBBY DUNBAR IN 2004?

A. He was living under a new identity
B. He had been abducted by a serial killer
C. He was never Bobby Dunbar
D. He had survived but lost his memory

239. WHAT SIGNIFICANT ACTION DID KATE MOIR TAKE THAT HELPED SOLVE THE BIRNIE MURDER SPREE?

A. She provided a detailed confession
B. She led police to the buried bodies
C. She escaped and alerted authorities
D. She identified the Birnies in a lineup

240. WHAT MOTIVATED RAY AND FAYE COPELAND TO MURDER THEIR VICTIMS?

A. Financial gain
B. Sexual gratification
C. Eliminating unwanted individuals
D. Revenge against society

241. WHERE DID THE AX MURDER HOUSE INCIDENT OCCUR?

A. Gloucester, England
B. Villisca, Iowa
C. Bavaria, Germany
D. Lake Michigan, USA

242. WHAT MADE THE AX MURDER HOUSE CASE SO HORRIFYING FOR THE MOORE FAMILY MEMBERS?

A. The killer used poison
B. The murders occurred in broad daylight
C. The family was unaware of the intruder until it was too late
D. The victims were mutilated beyond recognition

243. HOW DID KATE MOIR ESCAPE FROM THE BIRNIES AFTER BEING KIDNAPPED?

A. She overpowered David Birnie
B. She used a hidden weapon
C. She called the police from a grocery store
D. She fled into the wilderness

244. WHAT MOTIVE DID THE BIRNIES USE TO LURE THEIR VICTIMS INTO THE CAR?

A. Offering free meals
B. Pretending to be police officers
C. Offering a ride to church
D. Promising job opportunities

245. WHAT WAS THE FINAL ACTION TAKEN BY DAVID BIRNIE TO ENSURE DENISE BROWN'S DEATH AFTER SHE SAT UP IN HER GRAVE?

A. He dragged her out and left her
B. He strangled her with his bare hands
C. He struck her in the head with an ax
D. He burned the grave

246. WHAT CRIMINAL ACTION DID FRED WEST PERFORM ON HIS STEPDAUGHTER CHARMAINE?

A. He poisoned her
B. He strangled her
C. He beat her until she refused to cry
D. He set her on fire

247. WHAT EVENT LED TO THE ARREST OF IAN BRADY AND MYRA HINDLEY IN THE MOORS MURDERS CASE?

A. They confessed to all their crimes
B. A neighbor reported suspicious activities
C. Discovery of bodies in their garden
D. Surveillance footage caught them in the act

248. WHAT MADE THE GRUBER FAMILY MURDER CASE IN BAVARIA, GERMANY, PARTICULARLY HORRIFYING?

A. The use of poison
B. The absence of any signs of struggle
C. The stacking of bodies in the barn
D. The killer was never seen

249. WHAT UNUSUAL DETAIL SURROUNDED THE DISCOVERY OF THE ROBISON FAMILY'S BODIES IN LAKE MICHIGAN?

A. The bodies were found in a boat
B. There was no sign of forced entry
C. Their dog was the only survivor
D. The house was entirely burned down

250. WHAT MADE THE KEDDIE CABIN MURDERS CASE IN 1981 SO STRANGE?

A. Only one member of the family was killed
B. The victims were all found in different locations
C. The two younger brothers and one friend were unharmed
D. The cabin was found completely empty

251. WHAT WAS THE SIGNIFICANT ACTION TAKEN BY CHARMAINE, FRED WEST'S STEPDAUGHTER, THAT LED TO THE DISCOVERY OF WEST'S CRIMES?

A. She managed to escape and inform the police
B. She recorded her abuse and showed it to friends
C. She left evidence at the crime scene
D. She confessed to the authorities directly

252. WHAT UNSETTLING BEHAVIOR DID THE KEDDIE CABIN MURDERS PRESENT THAT MADE THE CASE EVEN MORE MYSTERIOUS?

A. The killer used multiple weapons
B. The younger siblings were unharmed
C. The victims were all related
D. The murders happened during a storm

253. WHAT SUSPECT WAS ARRESTED FOR THE ROBISON FAMILY MURDERS BUT NEVER TRIED?

A. Marty Smartt
B. Joseph Scolaro III
C. Bo Boubede
D. Emmett Monroe Spencer

254. WHAT ELEMENT MADE THE MURDERS AT THE AX MURDER HOUSE CASE SO GROTESQUE?

A. The use of multiple weapons
B. The presence of the killer in the home for hours
C. The victims were all related
D. The house was set on fire

255. WHAT UNSOLVED MYSTERY SURROUNDS THE MURDERS OF THE WALKER FAMILY?

A. The use of a unique weapon
B. The absence of any signs of struggle
C. The killer's identity remains unknown
D. The family was targeted for their wealth

256. WHAT CRITICAL EVIDENCE WAS MISSING FROM THE AX MURDER HOUSE SCENE THAT MADE THE CASE HARD TO SOLVE?

A. The murder weapon
B. Fingerprints
C. DNA samples
D. Witness testimonies

257. WHAT STRATEGY DID THE BIRNIES USE TO DISGUISE THEIR MURDERS AS NORMAL ACTS?

A. They hosted social gatherings
B. They staged robberies
C. They chained victims to beds and acted like family
D. They left cryptic messages at crime scenes

258. WHAT MADE THE ADE FAMILY MURDERS IN 1847 SO CHALLENGING TO SOLVE?

A. The lack of modern forensic methods
B. The murders were committed in multiple locations
C. The family had no enemies
D. The victims were all adults

259. WHAT DID THE KEDDIE CABIN MURDERS HAVE IN COMMON WITH THE AX MURDER HOUSE CASE?

A. Both involved the use of an ax
B. Both families were wealthy farmers
C. Both cases involved intruders staying inside the house
D. Both cases were solved quickly

260. HOW DID THE MOORS MURDERS GET THEIR NAME?

A. Because the victims were all farmers
B. Because the crimes took place in a moorland area
C. Because the killer wore a cloak
D. Because the victims were found in a swamp

261. WHAT CRIME DID JACOB ADE, THE PATRIARCH OF THE ADE FAMILY, BELIEVE LED TO THE MURDERS OF HIS FAMILY?

A. A family dispute over inheritance
B. A robbery gone wrong
C. Revenge against neighbors
D. Mental illness

262. WHAT FINAL ACTION DID RAY AND FAYE COPELAND TAKE BEFORE THEIR DEATHS?

A. They attempted to escape from prison
B. They confessed to their crimes
C. They committed suicide
D. They were executed by the state

263. HOW DID FAYE COPELAND'S ROLE IN THE CRIMES LEAD TO HER SENTENCING?

A. She was the mastermind behind the murders
B. She actively participated in all the killings
C. She provided logistical support and information
D. She turned herself in and confessed

264. WHAT WAS THE PRIMARY MOTIVE BEHIND THE ADE FAMILY MURDERS?

A. Revenge against neighbors
B. Desire for wealth
C. Mental instability
D. Religious fanaticism

265. WHAT SIGNIFICANCE DID THE PHONE CALL PLAY IN ENDING THE BIRNIES' MURDER SPREE?

A. It was a confession to the police
B. It provided crucial evidence linking them to the crimes
C. It alerted the authorities about Kate Moir's location
D. It was a ransom demand to the victims' families

266. WHAT UNIQUE MURDER METHOD DID THE ADE FAMILY FACE IN 1847?

A. Poisoning with a rare toxin
B. Decapitation and skull removal
C. Strangulation with a garrote
D. Burning the house down

267. HOW WERE THE GRIMES SISTERS FOUND AFTER THEIR DISAPPEARANCE?

A. In a deserted park
B. Along a snowy road
C. Inside an abandoned building
D. In their family home

268. WHAT MADE THE GRIMES SISTERS CASE SO STRANGE?

A. Their bodies were never found
B. Multiple conflicting autopsy reports
C. They were last seen with a famous celebrity
D. The crime scene was pristine

269. WHO WERE THE LAST PEOPLE TO SEE THE GRIMES SISTERS ALIVE?

A. Their classmates
B. A man resembling Elvis Presley
C. Family friends
D. Fellow moviegoers

270. WHAT DID THE AUTOPSIES OF THE GRIMES SISTERS INDICATE AS THE CAUSE OF DEATH?

A. Gunshot wounds
B. Drowning
C. Shock and exposure
D. Poisoning

271. WHY HAS THE GRIMES SISTERS CASE REMAINED UNSOLVED FOR SO LONG?

A. Lack of physical evidence
B. Witnesses were uncooperative
C. The killer was a famous person
D. Conflicting autopsy results

272. WHAT HORRIFIC ACT DID RUSSELL KEITH DARDEEN COMMIT BEFORE HIS DEATH?

A. Kidnapping his family
B. Removing his penis after being shot
C. Burning down his home
D. Poisoning his wife

273. WHAT MADE THE MURDER OF THE DARDEEN FAMILY SO MYSTERIOUS?

A. The family had no enemies
B. The murders occurred in broad daylight
C. Elaine was never pregnant
D. All family members survived

274. WHO WAS SUSPECTED BUT NEVER CHARGED IN THE DARDEEN FAMILY MURDERS?

A. Ian Brady
B. Myra Hindley
C. Tommy Lynn Sells
D. Ted Bundy

275. WHAT BIZARRE ACTION DID CLIVE PLAN TO REENACT IF JACK THE RIPPER WAS SELECTED ON THE THRILL-KILL WHEEL?

A. Poisoning a victim's drink
B. Eviscerating a victim with Masonic symbols
C. Setting a victim on fire
D. Strangling a victim in public

276. WHAT FINAL ACT LED TO THE ARREST OF IAN BRADY AND MYRA HINDLEY IN THE MOORS MURDERS?

A. A confession to a friend
B. A neighbor reporting suspicious activities
C. Discovery of bodies buried in their garden
D. Surveillance footage capturing their crimes

277. WHAT MYSTERIOUS EVENT PROMPTED THE INVESTIGATION OF THE FLANNAN ISLES LIGHTHOUSE?

A. A severe storm
B. The lighthouse light being extinguished
C. A shipwreck nearby
D. Unusual wildlife sightings

278. WHAT UNUSUAL SIGNS DID JOSEPH MOORE FIND WHEN HE INVESTIGATED THE FLANNAN ISLES LIGHTHOUSE?

A. The lighthouse was fully stocked with supplies
B. All doors were open and the lighthouse was bustling
C. Fires had not been lit in days and clocks had stopped
D. The keepers left personal belongings behind

279. WHAT REMAINDER DID GOVERNOR JOHN WHITE FIND THAT SUGGESTED A CONNECTION WITH THE INDIAN TRIBE CROATOAN AT ROANOKE ISLAND?

A. A carved cross
B. The word "Croatoan"
C. An abandoned canoe
D. Traditional Croatoan artifacts

280. WHAT MYSTERIOUS CONDITION WAS MARY REESER FOUND IN AFTER HER DEATH?

A. Her apartment was entirely burnt down
B. Her body was completely incinerated with no remains
C. Her body was burned with parts still intact, and no signs of a high-temperature fire
D. She disappeared without a trace

281. WHAT ACTION DID KEN MCELROY'S WIFE CLAIM TO HAVE WITNESSED DURING HIS MURDER IN SKIDMORE, MISSOURI?

A. She saw him arguing with the shooter
B. She saw the shooter in the crowd
C. She saw a specific individual firing the gun
D. She did not witness anything

282. HOW DID THE MAID AT THE HOTEL PRESIDENT BECOME INVOLVED IN THE MYSTERIOUS DEATH OF ROLAND T. OWEN?

A. She found his body first
B. She was present during the entire incident
C. She was the one to call the police
D. She interacted with him multiple times during his stay

283. WHAT MADE THE DEATH OF ROLAND T. OWEN (ARTEMUS OGLETREE) IN ROOM 1046 SO MYSTERIOUS?

A. His body was never found
B. The room was found locked from the outside
C. There were multiple attackers
D. He left a detailed confession

284. WHAT EVIDENCE FOUND IN MARY REESER'S APARTMENT CONTRADICTED THE THEORY OF A HIGH-TEMPERATURE FIRE?

A. Her belongings were untouched
B. The chair was still intact
C. Light switches and candlesticks had melted but other items remained

undamaged

D. There were no signs of forced entry

285. WHAT WAS THE OUTCOME OF THE INVESTIGATION INTO THE DISAPPEARANCE OF THE FLANNAN ISLES LIGHTHOUSE KEEPERS?

A. They were found alive years later

B. They were discovered to have been murdered by pirates

C. Their disappearance remains unexplained

D. It was revealed they left voluntarily to start new lives

286. WHAT MYSTERIOUS MARK DID GOVERNOR JOHN WHITE EXPECT TO FIND ON THE TREES IF THE ROANOKE COLONY WAS FORCED TO LEAVE?

A. A carved cross

B. The colony's flag

C. A set of footprints

D. A hidden map

287. HOW DID THE TOWNSPEOPLE OF SKIDMORE, MISSOURI, JUSTIFY THE KILLING OF KEN MCELROY WITHOUT ANY ARRESTS?

A. They claimed self-defense

B. They believed it was the only way to rid the town of his tyranny

C. They framed another individual for the murder

D. They thought the police were covering for him

288. WHAT DID THE HOTEL PRESIDENT MAID FIND WHEN SHE RETURNED TO CLEAN ROOM 1046 AFTER ROLAND T. OWEN HAD BEEN THERE?

A. The room was empty

B. Owen was peacefully sleeping

C. Owen was on the bed naked with a dark stain on the bedding

D. There was evidence of a struggle

289. WHAT DID THE MAID DISCOVER WHEN SHE RETURNED TO ROOM 1046 THE MORNING AFTER ROLAND T. OWEN'S FIRST VISIT?

A. Owen had left a detailed diary
B. The room was still clean and orderly
C. Owen was still in the room, sitting in the dark
D. There was a hidden passageway

290. WHAT WORD DID JOHN WHITE FIND THAT INDEED CARRIED A CLUE ABOUT THE FATE OF THE ROANOKE COLONY?

A. Absent
B. Survivor
C. Croatoan
D. Nowhere

291. WHAT RAISED SUSPECTS ABOUT THE CAUSE OF MARY REESER'S DEATH?

A. Lack of any fire evidence
B. Complete preservation of all her belongings
C. Her body was burned while other items remained mostly undamaged
D. She left a farewell note

292. WHAT MADE THE INVESTIGATION OF THE FLANNAN ISLES LIGHTHOUSE KEEPERS' DISAPPEARANCE SO CHALLENGING?

A. The lighthouse was easily accessible
B. There were no signs of forced entry or struggle
C. The keepers left personal messages
D. They were seen leaving the island shortly before

293. WHAT STRANGE PHENOMENON DID THE MAID ENCOUNTER IN ROOM 1046 AFTER ROLAND T. OWEN HAD BEEN THERE?

A. The room temperature was abnormally cold
B. Multiple voices were heard inside
C. Objects moved on their own
D. The room was filled with an unexplained fog

294. WHAT WAS THE PRIMARY THEORY FOR THE DISAPPEARANCE OF THE ROANOKE COLONY?

A. They were wiped out by a natural disaster
B. They returned to England
C. They assimilated with the Croatoan tribe
D. They were taken by pirates

295. WHAT EVIDENCE LED TO THE CONVICTION OF FRED AND ROSEMARY WEST?

A. Eyewitness testimonies
B. DNA evidence
C. Fred's own confession
D. Discovery of multiple human remains at their home

296. WHICH SERIAL KILLER WAS KILLED IN PRISON BY ANOTHER INMATE?

A. Jeffrey Dahmer
B. Daniel Camargo Barbosa
C. Albert DeSalvo
D. All of the Above

297. WHO WERE KNOWN AS THE TOOLBOX KILLERS?

A. Gerald and Charlene Gallego
B. Leonard Lake and Charles Ng
C. Lawrence Bittaker and Roy Norris
D. David and Catherine Birnie

298. TRUE OR FALSE: A "SILENCE OF THE LAMBS" ACTOR WAS SHOWN TAPES MADE BY THE TOOLBOX KILLERS?

299. WHICH OF THESE STATEMENTS ABOUT THE INVESTIGATION INTO ANDREI CHIKATILO'S CRIMES IS TRUE?

A. Another man was wrongly executed for Chikatilo's first murder
B. A woman accused of one of the murders fled to Poland
C. A suspect committed suicide while in custody
D. Both A and C

300. HOW WAS SERIAL KILLER JAVED IQBAL SENTENCED TO BE EXECUTED?

A. Fed to hungry leopards
B. Hanged with the same chain he used on his victims
C. Stoned to death by his victims' families
D. Set on fire

301. WHAT UNUSUAL JOB DID CANADIAN SERIAL KILLER BRUCE MCARTHUR HAVE?

A. Santa Claus
B. Camp counselor
C. Social worker
D. Pastor

302. TRUE OR FALSE: A FEMALE SERIAL KILLER IN CHINA WAS ON THE RUN FOR 20 YEARS BEFORE HER CAPTURE IN 2019.

303. WHAT DID THE MOTHER OF RODNEY ALCALA'S VICTIM PLAN TO DO DURING HIS FIRST MURDER TRIAL?

A. Dump red paint on Alcala's lawyers
B. Shoot Alcala in court
C. Lead a protest outside the courthouse
D. Both A and C

304. WHICH SERIAL KILLER ALSO APPEARED ON A TELEVISION GAME SHOW?

A. John Cooper
B. William Bonin
C. Dr. Harold Shipman
D. Samuel Little

305. WHICH SERIAL KILLER TOOK A PHOTO WITH A FIRST LADY OF THE U.S.?

A. John Wayne Gacy
B. Ted Bundy
C. Wayne Williams
D. Herb Baumeister

306. WHICH SERIAL KILLER ONCE SAVED SOMEONE'S LIFE?

A. Israel Keyes
B. Ted Bundy
C. Arthur Shawcross
D. Both B and C

307. WHAT MADE CHARLES MANSON UNIQUE AMONG SERIAL KILLERS?

A. He personally committed all his murders
B. He never physically killed anyone himself
C. He targeted only celebrities
D. He used poison as his primary method

308. WHERE DID CHARLES MANSON AND HIS FOLLOWERS RESIDE BEFORE COMMITTING THE MURDERS?

A. A suburban neighborhood in Los Angeles
B. Spahn's Movie Ranch, an abandoned film set
C. A farmhouse in rural California
D. An apartment complex in downtown LA

309. HOW DID THE LOS ANGELES POLICE FIRST CONNECT THE TATE AND LABIANCA MURDERS TO CHARLES MANSON?

A. DNA evidence linking Manson to the crime scenes
B. A confession from one of Manson's followers
C. Similar writings left at both crime scenes
D. Surveillance footage capturing Manson's presence

310. WHAT WAS THE OUTCOME OF CHARLES MANSON'S FIRST TRIAL?

A. He was acquitted of all charges
B. He was sentenced to death
C. He was sentenced to life in prison
D. His trial was declared a mistrial

311. WHAT METHOD DID GILBERT PAUL JORDAN USE TO KILL HIS VICTIMS?

A. Strangulation
B. Bludgeoning with blunt objects

C. Forcing excessive alcohol consumption
D. Poisoning with toxic substances

312. WHAT CRIMINAL CHARGE DID GILBERT PAUL JORDAN RECEIVE FOR HIS FIRST KNOWN MURDER?

A. First-degree murder
B. Manslaughter
C. Second-degree murder
D. No charge was filed

313. HOW WAS GILBERT PAUL JORDAN FINALLY ARRESTED FOR HIS CRIMES?

A. DNA evidence linked him to the murders
B. A witness came forward to identify him
C. His fingerprints were found at the crime scenes
D. He confessed to the police

314. WHAT WAS THE NICKNAME GIVEN TO DENNIS RADER DUE TO HIS MURDERS' MODUS OPERANDI?

A. The Night Stalker
B. The BTK Killer
C. The Zodiac Killer
D. The Green River Killer

315. HOW WAS DENNIS RADER IDENTIFIED AND CAPTURED IN 2005?

A. DNA evidence from a crime scene
B. Surveillance footage linking him to a murder
C. A floppy disk he sent to the police
D. A confession letter he wrote

316. WHAT METHOD DID AILEEN WUORNOS USE TO KILL HER VICTIMS?

A. Poisoning
B. Stabbing
C. Shooting
D. Strangulation

317. WHAT BACKGROUND FACTOR CONTRIBUTED TO AILEEN WUORNOS' PATH TO SERIAL KILLING?

A. She had a high-powered career
B. She experienced a stable and supportive childhood
C. She endured abuse and a tumultuous family life
D. She was diagnosed with multiple mental illnesses

318. WHAT FACTOR ALLOWED DENNIS RADER TO EVADE CAPTURE FOR DECADES?

A. He was highly mobile and traveled frequently
B. He used advanced technology to hide his identity
C. He maintained a façade of normalcy and blended into his community
D. He never left any physical evidence at crime scenes

319. HOW DID AILEEN WUORNOS' CRIMES COME TO LIGHT IN FLORIDA?

A. She turned herself in to the police
B. She was caught in the act of committing a murder
C. Police connected her fingerprints to multiple crime scenes
D. Witnesses identified her through an anonymous tip

320. WHAT INSIGHT DID PSYCHOLOGISTS GAIN FROM GILBERT PAUL JORDAN'S CASE?

A. The effectiveness of rehabilitation programs
B. The link between alcoholism and serial killing
C. The role of early childhood trauma in developing violent tendencies
D. The impact of financial success on criminal behavior

321. WHAT WAS THE FINAL SENTENCE GIVEN TO DENNIS RADER FOR HIS CRIMES AS THE BTK KILLER?

A. Death penalty
B. Life imprisonment without parole
C. 10 consecutive life terms
D. 25 years to life

322. HOW DID CHARLES MANSON VIEW HIS OWN ROLE WITHIN HIS CULT?

A. As a passive leader
B. As a figurehead with no real control
C. As the ultimate master of manipulation
D. As a spiritual guide with no violent intentions

323. WHAT SYMBOLIC MESSAGE DID CHARLES MANSON WANT TO LEAVE AT HIS MURDER SCENES?

A. His signature
B. Political slogans
C. Racially charged phrases like "Pig" and "War"
D. Religious symbols

324. WHAT FACTOR CONTRIBUTED TO GILBERT PAUL JORDAN'S ABILITY TO CONTINUE HIS CRIMINAL ACTIVITIES AFTER HIS RELEASE FROM PRISON?

A. His high intelligence
B. Lack of police resources
C. Lenient sentencing and early release
D. Support from influential community members

325. WHAT PSYCHOLOGICAL DIAGNOSIS WAS GIVEN TO GILBERT PAUL JORDAN BY DR. TIBOR BEZEREDI?

A. Schizophrenia
B. Bipolar disorder
C. Antisocial personality disorder
D. Narcissistic personality disorder

326. WHAT INHERITANCE ALLOWED GILBERT PAUL JORDAN TO HIRE THE BEST LAWYERS AND EXTEND HIS CRIMINAL ACTIVITY?

A. A successful business
B. Money left by a deceased relative
C. Earnings from his barber shop
D. Stock market investments

327. WHAT WAS THE PRIMARY MOTIVE BEHIND CHARLES MANSON'S ORDER TO MURDER SHARON TATE AND OTHERS?

A. Personal vendetta against the victims
B. Financial gain
C. To incite a race war known as "Helter Skelter"
D. To eliminate competition for his leadership

328. HOW DID DENNIS RADER FINALIZE HIS CONVICTION AS THE BTK KILLER?

A. By confessing to all his murders
B. Through DNA evidence linking him to the crime scenes
C. By matching his hair sample to DNA from the victims
D. Through surveillance footage capturing his actions

329. WHAT INCREASED THE CHANCES OF CHARLES MANSON'S MEMBERS BEING INDICTED FOR THE TATE AND LABIANCA MURDERS?

A. Physical evidence directly linking them to the crime scenes
B. Testimony from Susan Atkins and Linda Kasabian
C. Surveillance footage showing their presence at the scenes
D. Confessions from other cult members

330. WHAT DID AILEEN WUORNOS ADMIT DURING HER TRIAL THAT LED TO HER CONVICTION?

A. She confessed to all her murders
B. She provided detailed accounts of the murders
C. She admitted to six killings
D. She offered no confession but presented evidence against herself

ANSWERS

1. ANSWER: C. HE WAS A SERIAL KILLER WHO PREYED ON YOUNG BOYS.

John Wayne Gacy, the man behind the clown makeup, was a terrifying example of how appearances can be deceiving. A respected member of his community, Gacy used his friendly persona and "Pogo the Clown" alter ego to gain access to his victims – young boys whom he would lure to his home with promises of jobs or a place to stay. Once inside, Gacy would trick them into wearing handcuffs, then unleash a horrifying ordeal of rape and torture before ultimately strangling them. He buried many of his victims in the crawl space of his suburban Chicago home.

Gacy's reign of terror ended in 1978 when his final victim, 15-year-old Robert Piest, disappeared after going to see Gacy about a potential job. Piest's disappearance triggered an investigation that uncovered the horrifying truth about the "Killer Clown." Gacy was convicted of 33 murders and executed in 1994.

2. ANSWER: A. TRUE

After the horrifying crimes committed by Marc Dutroux in Belgium, many citizens who shared his last name sought to distance themselves from the association. According to reports, over one-third of Belgians with the surname Dutroux filed to change their names following the outrage sparked by Dutroux's actions and the perceived failure of law enforcement to prevent them. In 1996, over 300,000 Belgians marched in what became known as the White March to protest how authorities handled the case. In 2019, a similar protest, the Black March, occurred in response to the early release of Dutroux's accomplice, Michel Lelièvre. Dutroux remains imprisoned for life.

3. ANSWER: B. SHE WAS A PROFESSIONAL WRESTLER

Juana Barraza, infamously known as "La Mataviejitas" or "The Little Old Lady Killer," led a double life as a professional wrestler named "La Dama del Silencio" (The Lady of Silence). Between the late 1990s and 2006, Barraza preyed on elderly women, posing as a social worker to gain their trust before entering their homes and killing them, typically by strangulation. Authorities estimated that she murdered 48 women before she was caught after being spotted fleeing a crime scene by a neighbor.

4. ANSWER: B. DENNIS RADER

Known as BTK (Bind, Torture, Kill), Dennis Rader terrorized Wichita, Kansas, for years. In 1979, Rader stalked Anna Williams, cutting her phone lines and entering her home while she was away. After waiting for hours, she didn't return, and he left. Weeks later, Williams received a package containing some of her belongings along with a poem titled "Oh, Anna, Why Didn't You Appear?" In the end, Rader was convicted of 10 murders, but his obsession with Williams showed just how deep his desire for control ran.

5. ANSWER: D. TWITTER

Takahiro Shiraishi, known as the "Twitter Killer," used the social media platform to find suicidal individuals, luring them to his home under the guise of helping them end their lives. Between August and October 2017, he killed eight women and one man. Shiraishi promised that he would also die with them, but instead, he strangled them and dismembered their bodies. His gruesome crimes were uncovered on Halloween of 2017 when police discovered body parts in his apartment. Shiraishi was sentenced to death in 2020.

6. ANSWER: C. BY EVISCERATING THEM AND USING MASONIC SYMBOLS

If Jack the Ripper was selected, Clive intended to eviscerate his victim, incorporating Masonic symbols into the crime scene. This brutal method reflects the extreme violence and ritualistic nature associated with Ripper's legendary yet gruesome murders, showcasing Clive's obsession with accurate crime reconstruction.

7. ANSWER: B. REALIZING HE WAS BROODING TOO MUCH

Clive momentarily set aside his dark fantasies after recognizing he was spending too much time obsessing over serial killers. This self-awareness hinted at the internal struggle between his morbid interests and the realization of the danger he was putting himself in, heightening the tension and sense of impending doom.

8. ANSWER: B. THE EYEBALL KILLER

Clive admired the nickname "The Eyeball Killer," given to Texan Charles Albright, for its horrifying specificity and vivid imagery. This moniker, like "The Killer Clown," perfectly captured the terrifying essence of Albright's brutal methods, making it one of the most memorable and chilling nicknames in the annals of serial killer history.

9. ANSWER: B. THEY BOTH WANTED A SWIFT EXECUTION

Israel Keyes, a notorious serial killer, and Gary Gilmore, a convicted double murderer, shared the desire for a swift execution after their arrests. Keyes, who committed numerous murders across the U.S., expressed a wish for the death penalty and tried to arrange an expedited execution before committing suicide in 2012. Similarly, Gilmore refused appeals after his death sentence and demanded to be executed by firing squad, a sentence that was carried out in Utah in 1977.

10. ANSWER: C. JOSEPH KALLINGER

Joseph Kallinger enlisted his 13-year-old son Michael to join him on a crime spree in 1974. The pair broke into homes across multiple states, tied up women, sexually assaulted them, and ransacked the houses. During a home invasion in New Jersey, Kallinger murdered a nurse who had come to check on a neighbor. Kallinger was later caught after police found evidence linking him to the crime scenes. He was sentenced to life in prison, while Michael, considered under his father's control, was sentenced as a juvenile.

11. ANSWER: A. TRUE

Pedro Alonso López, known as the Monster of the Andes, and Daniel Camargo Barbosa, another notorious serial killer, were both held in Garcia Moreno prison in Quito, Ecuador. López, who confessed to killing around 300 girls, was imprisoned in 1980 and served 16 years. Meanwhile, Camargo, responsible for the murders of over 150 girls, was sentenced to 16 years in 1989. López was released in 1994, and Camargo was murdered by a fellow inmate the same year.

12. ANSWER: D. ALL OF THE ABOVE

Each of these killers was released from prison after serving time for previous murders, only to kill again. Kenneth McDuff murdered three teenagers in 1966 and was later paroled in 1989, only to resume killing. Edmund Kemper, who murdered his grandparents as a teenager, went on to kill eight women after his release. Arthur Shawcross, after serving 14 years for killing two children, murdered 12 women upon his release. These cases highlight the dangerous consequences of releasing violent offenders prematurely.

13. ANSWER: D. BOTH A AND C

The Stoneman, an unidentified killer from India, murdered homeless people in the 1980s by crushing their heads with heavy stones. Despite a string of deaths across cities like Mumbai and Kolkata, the case remains unsolved. Similarly, the Honolulu Strangler killed five women in Hawaii between 1985 and 1986. Though police had a prime suspect, the killer was never officially identified, and the case remains unsolved to this day.

14. ANSWER: A. TRUE

The urban legend of "Cropsey" haunted Staten Island for years, telling of a killer who preyed on children. This myth turned into a horrifying reality when Andre Rand was arrested for kidnapping 12-year-old Jennifer Schweiger in 1987. Rand, who had worked at the infamous Willowbrook State School, lived near the ruins where the legend of Cropsey was based. Though convicted for kidnapping, he is suspected of being involved in the disappearances and possible murders of other children. The 2009 documentary *Cropsey* explores how this urban myth came true.

15. ANSWER: C. HE REVISITED THEM FOR NECROPHILIC ACTS.

Ted Bundy, with his charm and good looks, shattered the myth of the monstrous serial killer. He was a law student, a social worker, even a suicide hotline volunteer – a man who could easily blend into everyday life. Yet, beneath this veneer of normalcy lurked a depraved killer who raped and murdered women across multiple states.

Bundy's crimes were marked by a chilling pattern: he would lure his victims, often young women, to secluded locations, bludgeon them, and then indulge in necrophilia. He would revisit the bodies of his victims, sometimes for days or even weeks, until decomposition made it impossible. This macabre ritual was Bundy's way of maintaining control and extending his power over his victims even after death.

Apprehended in 1978 after a series of escapes and further murders, Bundy was executed in Florida in 1989. His case continues to fascinate and horrify, a stark reminder of the darkness that can hide beneath a charming exterior.

16. ANSWER: A. MOST SERIAL KILLERS ARE LONERS

Contrary to popular belief, many serial killers are not the socially awkward loners we often imagine. Instead, they blend into society with ease. They can be charming, well-liked, and even have families. They attend church, work regular jobs, and coach Little League, hiding their dark sides in plain sight. Killers like Denis Rader (BTK) and Gary Ridgeway (The Green River Killer) led seemingly normal lives, yet they murdered 58 people between them.

17. ANSWER: B. THEY WERE CAPABLE OF HIDING IN PLAIN SIGHT WHILE LIVING NORMAL LIVES

Denis Rader, also known as BTK (Bind, Torture, Kill), and Gary Ridgeway, the Green River Killer, were not the stereotypical loners often associated with serial killers. They both maintained families and lived normal suburban lives, all while committing horrific murders. Rader, a church leader and family man, killed 10 people, while Ridgeway, also married with children, murdered at least 48 women.

18. ANSWER: C. HE RELEASED THEM INTO THE WILDERNESS AND HUNTED THEM LIKE ANIMALS

Robert Hansen, known as the Butcher Baker, was a sadistic serial killer who abducted women, raped them, and then took them into the wilderness in Alaska. After pretending to free them, Hansen would hunt his victims like prey, chasing them through the forests and shooting or stabbing them once he caught up. Over the years, Hansen raped more than 30 women and killed at least 17, all while maintaining the outward appearance of a regular family man.

19. ANSWER: C. AT LEAST 17

Robert Hansen, the "Butcher Baker," killed at least 17 women, though his total victim count is believed to be higher. His method was gruesome—after raping his victims, he would release them into the wild under the pretense of letting them go. Once they ran, Hansen would hunt them down, killing them like animals in the harsh Alaskan wilderness. His dual life as a husband and father only added to the horror of his crimes.

20. ANSWER: B. TO CREATE MINDLESS SEX SLAVES

Jeffrey Dahmer, known as the "Milwaukee Cannibal," killed 17 men between 1978 and 1991. His twisted goal was to turn his victims into mindless, submissive "zombies." He attempted to achieve this by drilling holes into their skulls and pouring acid or boiling water into their brains while they were still alive. These horrific attempts never worked. Dahmer also raped and, in some cases, ate his victims, keeping body parts like skulls and organs as trophies. His killing spree finally ended in 1991 when police discovered his gruesome apartment filled with body parts. Dahmer was convicted and later killed in prison in 1994.

21. ANSWER: D. A VICTIM ESCAPED AND ALERTED POLICE

Jeffrey Dahmer was nearly caught a month before his final arrest when one of his victims, 14-year-old Konerak Sinthasomphone, escaped from his apartment. Naked and bleeding, Konerak was found by two women who called the police. Despite their suspicions, the officers allowed Dahmer to take Konerak back to his apartment, convinced by Dahmer's claim that the boy was his boyfriend. Tragically, the officers never checked the apartment thoroughly, leaving Konerak to his fate. Dahmer killed him shortly after. He was finally arrested when another intended victim managed to escape and led the police back to Dahmer's apartment, revealing the horrors inside.

22. ANSWER: C. RICHARD RAMIREZ

Richard Ramirez, also known as the "Night Stalker," was a serial killer who terrorized Los Angeles in the mid-1980s. He earned his nickname by breaking into homes at night and brutally murdering his victims. His crimes included both murder and rape, and his victims ranged from young adults to the elderly. Ramirez had a disturbed upbringing, witnessing violence from a young age, which may have contributed to his homicidal tendencies. He was convicted of 13 murders in 1989 and sentenced to death. Ramirez showed no remorse and died of cancer while awaiting execution in 2013.

23. ANSWER: B. H.H. HOLMES

H.H. Holmes, considered America's first known serial killer, built a "Murder Castle" in Chicago during the 1893 World's Fair. The building, which appeared to be a hotel and retail space, was a nightmarish labyrinth with hidden rooms, trap doors, and secret passageways. Holmes lured victims, mostly women, into the upper floors where he would torture and kill them in soundproof rooms fitted with gas lines. After murdering them, he disposed of the bodies by dissecting them and selling their skeletons to medical schools. Holmes was finally arrested for insurance fraud but was also convicted of murdering his business partner, Ben Pitezel, and three of Pitezel's children. He was executed in 1896.

24. ANSWER: B. A BELT MADE FROM FEMALE NIPPLES

Ed Gein, the inspiration behind horror icons like Leatherface and Norman Bates, was arrested in 1957 for the murder of Bernice Worden. However, what the police found inside his home was far more horrifying than just a murder weapon. His house was filled with human remains—furniture made of bones, skulls used as bowls, and a belt made from female nipples. He confessed to robbing graves and fashioning objects from the bodies, but he only admitted to killing two women. Gein was deemed mentally unfit for trial and spent the rest of his life in a mental institution, where he died in 1984.

25. ANSWER: C. THEY ALLOWED DAHMER TO TAKE HIM BACK TO HIS APARTMENT

In one of the most tragic mistakes in modern policing, officers allowed Jeffrey Dahmer to take 14-year-old Konerak Sinthasomphone back to his apartment despite the boy being naked, confused, and bleeding. Dahmer convinced the officers that Konerak was his boyfriend and they had a simple argument. Without questioning the boy or investigating the strange smells from Dahmer's apartment, they left him in Dahmer's custody. Konerak was killed shortly afterward, and his body joined the others in Dahmer's apartment.

26. ANSWER: C. HE WAS DEFIANT AND UNREMORSEFUL

Richard Ramirez, also known as the "Night Stalker," showed no remorse for the brutal murders and rapes he committed in the 1980s. A self-proclaimed Satanist, Ramirez shrugged off his death sentence, telling the courtroom that "death always went with the territory." His complete lack of empathy or guilt made him one of the most terrifying killers in U.S. history. He was convicted of 13 murders but is suspected of many more. Ramirez died of cancer in 2013 while on death row.

27. ANSWER: B. FINANCIAL GAIN THROUGH INSURANCE FRAUD

While H.H. Holmes' "Murder Castle" may seem like a den of purely sadistic terror, much of his motivation came from financial greed. He often lured victims, particularly women, with promises of marriage or employment, only to kill them after securing control of their finances or life insurance policies. Holmes conducted multiple insurance scams and frauds, which eventually led to his downfall and arrest. While his murder spree was horrifying, his ultimate goal was often tied to monetary gain.

28. ANSWER: C. AN UNIDENTIFIED SERIAL KILLER

Jack the Ripper is one of the most infamous yet unidentified serial killers in history. Active in 1888, he brutally murdered and mutilated his victims in London's Whitechapel district. His victims' throats were cut, and their bodies dismembered in ways that suggested the killer had knowledge of human anatomy. Despite numerous theories over the years, no one was ever caught, and the case remains one of the greatest unsolved mysteries in criminal history.

29. ANSWER: B. MURDERING YOUNG WOMEN

Elizabeth Bathory, often referred to as the "Blood Countess," is remembered as one of the most notorious female serial killers. Living in Hungary during the 16th and 17th centuries, she allegedly tortured and killed hundreds of young women. It was said she believed bathing in their blood would preserve her youth. Although she was never formally tried for her crimes, Bathory was confined to her castle until her death, forever immortalized in both history and folklore.

30. ANSWER: C. "I WISH THE WORLD HAD ONE NECK SO I COULD CHOKE IT."

Carl Panzram was one of the most violent and remorseless serial killers of the early 20th century. Known for his hatred of humanity, he claimed to have killed at least 21 people. His last words reflected his deep disdain for the human race, as he said he wished he could kill everyone at once. He was executed in 1930, having shown no remorse for his crimes, including murder, rape, and burglary.

31. ANSWER: A. AILEEN WUORNOS

Aileen Wuornos, considered America's first female serial killer, was convicted of killing at least six men between 1989 and 1990. A prostitute, she claimed that she killed her victims in self-defense. Wuornos' story became the subject of multiple books, documentaries, and even an opera, highlighting the public's fascination with her troubled life and crimes. Despite her claim of self-defense, she showed no remorse for her actions, and her case remains one of the most sensationalized in criminal history.

32. ANSWER: C. USED HER HEAD AS A DARTBOARD

Ed Kemper, also known as the "Co-ed Killer," had a particularly brutal relationship with his mother, whom he resented deeply. In 1973, he killed her by beating her to death with a hammer, then decapitated her and used her severed head as a dartboard. He also cut out her vocal cords and attempted to dispose of them in the garbage disposal. Kemper, who had already murdered young women, confessed to his crimes, showing no remorse. He remains one of the most terrifying figures in the world of serial killers.

33. ANSWER: B. HE LEFT HIS VICTIMS NEAR THE GREEN RIVER

Gary Leon Ridgway, known as the Green River Killer, was named after the river where his first five victims were found. He is believed to have murdered at least 71 women, many of them prostitutes, between 1980 and 1990. Ridgway strangled his victims and often revisited their corpses to engage in necrophilia. His deep-seated hatred for women, particularly prostitutes, stemmed from a complicated and conflicting relationship with his mother. Ridgway was arrested in 2001 and confessed to the murders, receiving multiple life sentences.

34. ANSWER: D. POSSIBLY, BUT IT WAS NEVER PROVEN

Larry Hall, suspected of being one of the most prolific serial killers in U.S. history, confessed to over 35 murders but later recanted many of his statements. His twin brother, Gary, has denied any involvement, but some speculate that he may have known more about Larry's crimes than he let on. Larry Hall remains in prison, convicted of kidnapping, but the true extent of his murders remains uncertain, leaving many families without closure.

35. ANSWER: C. JOHN WAYNE GACY

Robin Gecht, the leader of the notorious Chicago Ripper Crew, once worked as a subcontractor for John Wayne Gacy. The Ripper Crew was responsible for terrorizing Chicago in the 1980s, abducting and murdering up to 20 women. Though no direct criminal connection was ever proven between Gecht and Gacy, it remains a chilling coincidence that Gecht worked for another infamous serial killer.

36. ANSWER: B. DENNIS NILSEN

Dennis Nilsen, a British serial killer active between 1978 and 1983, was finally caught when a plumber discovered human remains clogging the drains of his building. Nilsen had been killing young men he lured from bars and dismembering their bodies. Neighbors complained about the plumbing, and when human flesh was found in the pipes, it led police to Nilsen's apartment, where the stench of death was overwhelming. He confessed to murdering 15 men, though only 11 bodies were ever recovered.

37. ANSWER: D. ALL OF THE ABOVE

In the 1870s, the Bender family became infamous for murdering travelers who stayed at their inn in Kansas. The family, consisting of John Sr., Elvira, Kate, and John Jr., would rob and kill their guests, later burying the bodies on their property. Kate, the daughter, claimed to be a psychic and even offered to help the brother of one of their victims. The family fled once suspicions grew, and they were never apprehended, making them one of America's earliest known serial killer families.

38. ANSWER: B. CATHERINE EDDOWES' SHAWL

In 2019, forensic scientists claimed to have made a breakthrough in the infamous Jack the Ripper case by testing DNA from a shawl allegedly found near the body of victim Catherine Eddowes. The results pointed to Aaron Kosminski, a Polish barber who has long been a suspect in the case. However, many experts and "Ripperologists" question the shawl's authenticity and the validity of the findings.

39. ANSWER: C. FEMALE SERIAL KILLERS DON'T EXIST

Dr. Eric Hickey, a criminologist, once presented FBI agents with details of a poisoner whom he believed to be a female serial killer. The agents dismissed his theory, stating that "female serial killers do not exist." Hickey later proved them wrong, as the killer turned out to be Dorothea Puente, a woman who murdered her tenants for financial gain.

40. ANSWER: C. HER KEYS

In March 1985, Richard Ramirez, the notorious "Night Stalker," attempted to kill Maria Hernandez as she entered her home. Ramirez fired his gun at close range, but the bullet struck her keys, which she had raised to shield herself. The impact of the keys saved her life, and although her roommate was not so lucky, Hernandez survived to testify against Ramirez at his trial.

41. ANSWER: C. BOTH A AND B

The "Monster of Florence" is an unidentified killer (or killers) responsible for the deaths of eight couples between 1968 and 1985 in Tuscany. After the final crime, the killer mailed parts of the female victim to a prosecutor. Many speculate that the Monster of Florence may be the same person as California's Zodiac Killer, though this theory remains unproven.

42. ANSWER: B. A CODED LIST BELIEVED TO REFERENCE HIS VICTIMS

Randy Kraft, known as the "Scorecard Killer," was arrested in 1983 after police found a mysterious list in his car. The list, which contained 61 cryptic entries, was believed to reference his victims, with phrases like "Portland Blood" and "Hollywood Bus." Kraft was convicted of 16 murders, though authorities suspect the real number could be higher.

43. ANSWER: D. PEE WEE GASKINS

Donald "Pee Wee" Gaskins, a South Carolina serial killer, drove around in a purple hearse with a sign that read, "We haul anything, living or dead." Gaskins was responsible for the deaths of at least 14 people, though he claimed to have killed over 100. He was executed in 1991 after being convicted of multiple murders, including those he committed while on death row.

44. ANSWER: D. ALL OF THE ABOVE

Cary Stayner is best known for murdering four women near Yosemite National Park in 1999. What makes his case particularly tragic is that his younger brother, Steven Stayner, had been kidnapped and held captive for seven years before escaping. After his arrest, Cary Stayner demanded access to child pornography in exchange for his confession, though law enforcement refused. Despite his disturbing request, Stayner still confessed and is currently on death row.

45. ANSWER: A. USED POISON TO KILL HER SPOUSES AND SON

Daisy de Melker, recognized as one of South Africa's earliest female serial killers, systematically poisoned two of her three husbands and her son. As a nurse, she employed strychnine to eliminate her husbands, aiming to collect their life insurance payouts. Later, she used arsenic to murder her 20-year-old son, who she suspected was inquiring about his father's inheritance. While Daisy was convicted for her son's murder, the evidence was insufficient to convict her for the killings of her husbands. Ultimately, she was executed in 1932, leaving behind a legacy of deceit and tragedy.

46. ANSWER: B. A BALL-PEIN HAMMER

Peter Sutcliffe, the Yorkshire Ripper, employed a ball-pein hammer to brutally murder his victims. His choice of weapon was both crude and effective, allowing him to inflict severe damage and terrorize his victims with sheer force and violence.

47. ANSWER: A. HIS ABILITY TO EVADE CAPTURE

Jack the Ripper remains one of history's most infamous serial killers due to his complete evasion of law enforcement. Operating in 1888 London, his inability to be caught despite widespread fear and media attention cemented his status as a legendary and terrifying figure.

48. ANSWER: B. DENISE BROWN

Denise Brown, a 21-year-old woman, fell victim to Catherine and David Birnie's horrifying murder spree. After accepting a ride from them, Denise was brutally raped and stabbed by David. Believing she was dead, the Birnies buried her in a shallow grave. However, Denise's survival instinct kicked in, and she sat up in her grave, prompting David to strike her with an ax to ensure her death. This gruesome act became a signature of their cruel modus operandi, marking one of the darkest chapters in Australian criminal history.

49. ANSWER: C. SHE CALLED THE POLICE FROM A GROCERY STORE

Kate Moir was the sole survivor of Catherine and David Birnie's brutal attacks. After being chained and raped by David, Catherine momentarily left her to answer the doorbell, providing Kate with a fleeting opportunity to escape. Seizing this chance, Kate jumped out of the window and fled to the nearest grocery store, where she successfully contacted the police. Her courageous act led to the Birnies' swift arrest, bringing an end to their reign of terror and saving countless potential victims.

50. ANSWER: B. GROWING UP IN AN INCESTUOUS HOUSEHOLD

Fred West's path to becoming one of Britain's most infamous serial killers began in a deeply disturbed household. Exposed to incest and sexual abuse by both his father and mother from a young age, Fred developed severe psychological issues. These traumatic experiences distorted his understanding of relationships and normalcy, leading him to engage in horrific acts of violence and sexual abuse alongside his wife, Rosemary West. Their combined depravity resulted in the torture and murder of twelve young girls and women, leaving an indelible mark on Gloucester's history.

51. ANSWER: B. STRANGULATION AND TORTURE

Ian Brady and Myra Hindley, known as the Moors Murderers, employed strangulation and torture as their primary methods of killing. Operating between 1963 and 1965, they abducted, raped, and murdered twelve girls and young women, burying many of them along Saddleworth Moor. Their sadistic approach involved prolonged periods of abuse before ending their victims' lives, creating an atmosphere of fear and uncertainty in the community. Their eventual capture was the result of a failed attempt to implicate Myra's younger brother, leading to a thorough investigation that unearthed the remains of their victims.

52. ANSWER: B. THEY MURDERED FIVE DRIFTERS THEY HIRED

Ray and Faye Copeland became the oldest couple ever sentenced to death in the United States for the murders of at least five drifters. Operating between 1968 and

1983, they lured their victims under the pretense of employment opportunities. Once isolated, Ray brutally killed the men, while Faye's exact role remained ambiguous. A list of their victims' names, marked with Xs in Faye's handwriting, suggested her complicity. Despite their death sentences, both died in prison before the sentences could be carried out—Ray from natural causes and Faye from a stroke after being released to a nursing home.

53. ANSWER: B. THEY ENGAGED IN A SEXUAL RELATIONSHIP WHILE KILLING TOGETHER

Ottis Elwood Toole and Henry Lee Lucas formed a deadly partnership that allegedly resulted in the murder of over a hundred people. Meeting in 1976, their relationship was both sexual and criminal, with both men influencing each other's violent tendencies. Despite numerous confessions, much of their collaboration remains unverified due to their notorious dishonesty. Their combined notoriety makes them one of America's most infamous serial killer duos, shrouded in mystery and fear.

54. ANSWER: C. SHE BEAT HER UNTIL SHE REFUSED TO CRY

Rosemary West subjected her stepdaughter Charmaine to relentless physical abuse, brutally beating her until she stopped crying. This extreme violence was part of a larger pattern of torture and murder carried out by Rosemary and her husband, Fred West. Their sadistic acts included rape and the eventual disappearance of Charmaine, marking them as one of the most heinous serial killer couples in history. Their crimes left a lasting scar on Gloucester, revealing the depths of their depravity.

55. ANSWER: B. INCORPORATING MASONIC SYMBOLS

Clive, obsessed with accurately reconstructing serial killers' methods, intended to integrate Masonic symbols into his reenactment of Jack the Ripper's murders. This addition reflected his desire to add ritualistic and symbolic elements to the brutality, highlighting the meticulous nature of some serial killers. By embedding such dark symbolism, Clive aimed to deepen the authenticity and horror of his crime reconstructions, showcasing his twisted fascination with their gruesome acts.

56. ANSWER: C. TO CREATE A PHOTOGRAPHIC RECORD OF HIS DOMINANCE

Ian Brady took disturbing photographs of his victims during the Moors Murders to document his dominance and control over them. These pictures served as a macabre testament to his sadistic pleasure in torturing and killing young girls and women. The photographic evidence not only provided a chilling insight into Brady's mind but also became crucial in understanding the extent of his and Myra Hindley's depraved crimes, ultimately leading to their arrest and conviction.

57. ANSWER: C. DISCOVERY OF BODIES IN THEIR GARDEN

Ian Brady and Myra Hindley were ultimately captured when police obtained a search warrant for their home and discovered the remains of several victims buried in their garden. This gruesome find provided the necessary evidence to convict the couple of their heinous crimes. The unearthing of the bodies along Saddleworth Moor exposed the full extent of their murderous spree, ending their reign of terror and ensuring they would never harm another victim.

58. ANSWER: D. DOROTHEA PUENTE

Dorothea Puente operated a boarding house in California during the 1980s, presenting herself as a caring and supportive woman to those in need, particularly the homeless and addicted. Beneath this facade, Puente poisoned several tenants to steal their Social Security checks. Unlike "Angels of Death" like Jane Toppan, Charles Cullen, and Kristen Gilbert, who typically kill those under their medical care, Puente's motives were purely financial. She was convicted for three murders and died in prison in 2011, marking her as a distinct type of serial killer driven by greed rather than a medical or caregiving environment.

59. ANSWER: B. A SURVIVOR IDENTIFIED MILAT

In 1990, Paul Onions, a British tourist in Australia, was abducted by Ivan Milat, who posed as "Bill" during the ride. Onions managed to escape the vehicle and reported the incident, but the police initially did not pursue the case. Years later, following the discovery of seven bodies in Belanglo State Forest between 1992 and 1993, Onions recalled his encounter with Milat. His detailed testimony enabled authorities to identify and convict Milat in 1996. Ivan Milat was sentenced to life imprisonment and remained incarcerated until his death in 2019, closing one of Australia's most notorious serial killer cases.

60. ANSWER: TRUE

In 2010, Matthew Milat, the great-nephew of infamous serial killer Ivan Milat, committed murder by torturing and killing his friend David Auchterlonie with an ax in Belanglo State Forest. Alongside his accomplice, Cohen Klein, Matthew lured Auchterlonie under the pretense of celebrating his 17th birthday. Instead, he subjected his friend to brutal torture before murdering him. Matthew proudly declared he was continuing his family's murderous legacy. He was subsequently convicted and sentenced to 43 years in prison, highlighting the disturbing continuation of violence within the Milat family.

61. ANSWER: D. ALL OF THE ABOVE

Three women showcased incredible resilience by surviving attacks from notorious serial killers. Corazon Amurao was the sole survivor of Richard Speck's 1966 massacre, hiding under beds as Speck killed eight nurses. Carol DaRonch narrowly escaped Ted Bundy's attempt to abduct her by fleeing his car and surviving his assault. Tiffany Taylor survived an attack by New Jersey serial killer Khalil Wheeler-Weaver in 2016, ultimately leading to his conviction after she bravely testified despite initial threats from the police. Each of these women played pivotal roles in the trials that brought their attackers to justice, demonstrating remarkable courage in the face of extreme danger.

62. ANSWER: C. POLICE STOPPED HIM FOR A MISSING LICENSE PLATE AND DISCOVERED A BODY

In 1993, New York State troopers attempted to pull over Joel Rifkin because his truck was missing a rear license plate. During the traffic stop, officers detected a foul odor of decomposition emanating from the vehicle and discovered the body of Tiffany Bresciani, a girlfriend of punk singer David Rubinstein, in the truck bed. Rifkin confessed to murdering 17 women, leading to his life sentence. This routine traffic stop was the pivotal moment that exposed Rifkin's extensive killing spree, making him one of New York's most infamous serial killers.

63. ANSWER: TRUE

During his high school years, Jeffrey Dahmer engaged in pranks by inserting himself into multiple yearbook photos, including those for the National Honor Society, despite not being a member. The club advisor eventually noticed and had Dahmer's face obscured in the published photo. However, the original image resurfaced after Dahmer's arrest, misleadingly suggesting he was a loner. In reality, classmates remembered Dahmer as an active participant in typical high school activities, debunking the false narrative presented by the altered photo.

64. ANSWER: B. MYRA HINDLEY AND ROSEMARY WEST

The 2020 documentary "Rose West and Myra Hindley: The Untold Story" revealed that Rose West and Myra Hindley, two of the United Kingdom's most infamous female serial killers, were romantically involved while incarcerated together. Testimonies from Rose West's defense lawyer and a former inmate confirmed their affair. However, the relationship was short-lived as Hindley recognized Rose West's manipulative and dangerous nature, especially after West had already committed heinous acts, including the murder of her own children.

65. ANSWER: D. ALL OF THE ABOVE

Marc Dutroux, a Belgian serial killer, was convicted in 1989 for five sexual assaults but served only three years of his 13-year sentence. After his release, Dutroux embarked on a series of brutal crimes in 1995, kidnapping and murdering multiple young girls in Belanglo State Forest. His mother had informed authorities that Dutroux was holding two girls captive, but the search was unsuccessful, and those girls later died of starvation in his basement. In May 1996, Dutroux kidnapped another girl, Sabine Dardenne, and then Laetitia Delhez. Thanks to a witness who noted his license plate, both Sabine and Laetitia were rescued, leading to Dutroux's final conviction and life sentence. His case ignited widespread outrage and demands for justice reform in Belgium.

66. ANSWER: B. "I'M SAILING WITH THE ROCK, AND I'LL BE NEXT LIKE 'INDEPENDENCE DAY'"

Aileen Wuornos, a notorious American serial killer, faced execution by lethal injection in October 2002. Before her death, Wuornos delivered a perplexing statement: "I'm sailing with the Rock, and I'll be NEXT like 'Independence Day' with Jesus, June 6, like the movie, big mother ship and all. I'll be NEXT." The true meaning behind her enigmatic words remains unclear, though it's believed that "the Rock" symbolizes Jesus. Wuornos was convicted in Florida for the murders of seven men, leaving behind a legacy of confusion and terror with her cryptic final words.

67. ANSWER: D. BOTH A AND B

The Rochester Alphabet Murders, spanning from 1971 to 1973 in New York, involved the killing of three young girls—Carmen Colón, Wanda Walkowicz, and Michelle Maenza—each found in towns that shared the initial letter of their names: Chili, Webster, and Macedon, respectively. In 2007, authorities exhumed the remains of a suspected firefighter who had died by suicide, but DNA testing revealed no match to the evidence from the crimes. Similarly, in 2011, serial killer Joseph Naso was considered a suspect due to DNA links, yet his genetic material did not correspond with that of the victims. The case remains unsolved, with multiple suspects and the possibility of more than one perpetrator still under investigation.

68. ANSWER: C. KENNETH BIANCHI

In 1979, Kenneth Bianchi, infamously known as the Hillside Strangler, was identified as a suspect in the Rochester Alphabet Murders, which involved the deaths of three young girls with matching initials. Bianchi, who later committed multiple murders in California alongside his cousin, consistently denied any involvement in the Rochester crimes. Despite extensive investigations, DNA evidence did not link him to the murders. Nevertheless, authorities have not entirely dismissed his potential connection, considering the possibility of multiple perpetrators in the case.

69. ANSWER: B. HIS CURRENT LOCATION AND STATUS ARE UNKNOWN

Pedro Alonso López, notoriously dubbed the "Monster of the Andes," confessed to the brutal murder and rape of up to 300 young girls between the ages of eight and twelve across Colombia, Ecuador, and Peru. Arrested in Ecuador in 1980, López received a 16-year sentence but served only 14 years before being deported to Colombia. After four years of psychiatric treatment, he was released in 1998. Despite Interpol warrants issued in 2002, López's whereabouts remain a mystery. Subsequent murders with similar methods suggest he may still be active, but his fate and location are still unknown.

70. ANSWER: D. ALL OF THE ABOVE

The Snowtown Murders, uncovered in 1999 in South Australia, horrified the world when police discovered eight decomposed bodies stored in barrels within an abandoned bank building. The murders were orchestrated by four men—John

Bunting, Robert Wagner, James Vlassakis, and Mark Haydon—who believed they were eliminating pedophiles based on flimsy evidence. The gruesome nature of the crimes led to the conviction of all four perpetrators, with John Bunting receiving the most severe sentence for 11 homicides. In the aftermath, there was a proposal to rename Snowtown to Rosetown to dissociate the town's name from the horrific events.

71. ANSWER: C. DENNIS NILSEN

Dennis Nilsen, a British serial killer responsible for the murders of 15 young men, was allowed to keep two pet parakeets named Tweetles and Hamish while incarcerated. Audio recordings capture him interacting affectionately with his birds, showcasing a peculiar aspect of his prison life. Beyond caring for his pets, Nilsen spent his time documenting his life story and playing the keyboard. He remained in prison until his death in 2018, leaving behind a legacy of horror intertwined with unusual companionship.

72. ANSWER: TRUE

Joseph Kallinger, a convicted rapist and murderer, made shocking admissions in his 1983 book "The Shoemaker: The Anatomy of a Psychotic," wherein he confessed to killing his 14-year-old son, Joseph Jr., and a neighborhood boy in 1974. These confessions prompted authorities to charge him with these additional murders. Kallinger was subsequently convicted in 1984, solidifying his status as a serial killer. His chilling admissions provided crucial evidence that linked him to the crimes, revealing the depths of his psychopathy.

73. ANSWER: A. HE FEIGNED AN EPILEPTIC ATTACK

Yoo Young-chul, infamously known as South Korea's Raincoat Killer, terrorized the country in the early 2000s by murdering wealthy individuals and later targeting sex workers. Upon his arrest in 2004, Yoo ingeniously faked an epileptic seizure to attempt an escape. However, law enforcement swiftly recaptured him within 12 hours. Yoo confessed to 26 murders, including dismemberment and cannibalism, revealing a deeply disturbed psyche influenced by reading about another South Korean serial killer, Jeong Du-yeong.

74. ANSWER: B. KIMCHI

To conceal the foul smell of decomposition after dismembering his victims, Yoo Young-chul, the Raincoat Killer, employed kimchi, a traditional Korean dish known for its strong odor. He placed the remains in separate plastic bags and added kimchi to effectively mask the scent. When questioned about the unusual smell during his arrest, Yoo claimed it was a homemade special batch of kimchi made by his mother, cleverly diverting suspicion away from his heinous acts.

75. ANSWER: FALSE

Ann Rule was already an established crime writer when she encountered Ted Bundy while working at a crisis center in Seattle. Under a pen name, she contributed to “True Detective” magazine, covering various criminal cases. Her close relationship with Bundy led her to write “The Stranger Beside Me,” a book that delved into her friendship with him and his subsequent crimes. Therefore, her career as a crime writer was not developed as a result of her interactions with Bundy; she was already pursuing this path prior to meeting him.

76. ANSWER: B. SEAMSTRESSING WITH HUMAN SKIN

Ed Gein, notoriously known for his gruesome crimes, possessed a horrifying talent as a seamstress. Unlike ordinary seamstresses, Gein crafted macabre items such as a belt made from nipples, a lampshade fashioned from a victim's face, and chairs upholstered entirely in human skin. His craftsmanship, though terrifying, showcased a twisted precision that went unnoticed beyond the horrifying nature of his actions. This disturbing skill set him apart and cemented his place as one of history’s most infamous serial killers.

77. ANSWER: B. LEATHERFACE, NORMAN BATES, AND BUFFALO BILL

Ed Gein’s heinous crimes left an indelible mark on popular culture, inspiring some of horror’s most iconic characters. Leatherface from "The Texas Chainsaw Massacre," Norman Bates from "Psycho," and Buffalo Bill from "Silence of the Lambs" all draw heavily from Gein’s real-life acts of murder, grave-robbing, and skin-removal. These fictional killers embody the grotesque legacy of Gein, blending his meticulous craftsmanship with monstrous brutality to create enduring symbols of fear in the horror genre.

78. ANSWER: C. HE HIGHLIGHTED GEIN’S CRAFTSMANSHIP AND PERSONAL TRAITS

Clive took a unique approach in his biography of Ed Gein by emphasizing aspects of Gein's life that were often overlooked by other writers. Instead of solely detailing Gein's gruesome crimes, Clive celebrated his skill as a seamstress, his role as a loving son, and his dedication to research on diverse subjects. This approach aimed to humanize Gein, providing a more nuanced portrayal that delved into the complexities behind his monstrous actions, rather than just the horror of his deeds.

79. ANSWER: C. ABUSIVE CHILDHOODS AND EARLY WARNING SIGNS

In his exploration of serial killers, Clive consistently identified abusive childhoods and early warning signs as common traits among these individuals. Many of the killers he studied had histories of childhood abuse, bedwetting beyond the typical age, cruelty to animals, fascination with fire, and other disturbing behaviors. While these traits do not guarantee that someone will become a serial killer, they serve as significant indicators of potential future violence, underscoring the impact of early trauma on the development of such predators.

80. ANSWER: B. HE EXPERIENCED ABUSIVE PARENTS AND EXHIBITED EARLY WARNING SIGNS

Clive's personal experiences mirrored the traits he studied in serial killers, adding a layer of introspection to his work. Raised by abusive parents, Clive suffered minor head trauma and struggled with bedwetting until his mid-teens. He exhibited behaviors such as lighting small fires and setting rat traps, which are often associated with potential serial killers. Additionally, Clive was a loner who enjoyed pornography and horror films, further aligning his personal history with the profiles of the criminals he researched. These similarities provided him with a unique perspective, deepening his understanding of the psychological factors that contribute to serial killing.

81. ANSWER: C. THE KILLER CLOWN

John Wayne Gacy, notoriously known as "The Killer Clown," terrorized Chicago by leading a double life that masked his murderous nature. From 1972 to 1978, Gacy raped, tortured, and murdered 33 young boys and men, luring them into his home under the guise of being a respectable community member. Gacy's public persona as Pogo the Clown, performing at children's parties and charity events, gave him easy access to his victims. Once inside his house, Gacy tricked his targets into wearing handcuffs under the pretense of performing a "magic trick." What followed was sheer horror—rape, torture, and eventually, strangulation. Gacy buried 26 of his victims beneath his house. He was arrested in 1978, convicted in 1980, and executed in 1994. His chilling legacy remains one of the most disturbing in true crime history.

82. ANSWER: B. STRANGLING AFTER HAVING SEX

Clive's grim anticipation involved mimicking Dennis Nilsen's method of strangling victims post-coital. This twisted act reflects Nilsen's depraved pleasure in both sexual assault and murder, showcasing the disturbing blend of intimacy and violence that defines serial killing.

83. ANSWER: C. DEREK DEMANDED CLIVE ATTEND HIS SHOW INSTEAD OF WRITING

Derek, Clive's brother, significantly disrupted Clive's writing process by insisting that Clive attend and assist with his show, "Conversations with Dead Friends," at the Playhouse. Derek expected Clive to help with hot readings and after-show sales, pulling him away from his focused work on the Ed Gein biography. This tension highlighted the challenges Clive faced in balancing his dedication to documenting serial killers with his personal obligations and familial relationships, adding complexity to his character and motivations.

84. ANSWER: C. A LAMPSHADE MADE FROM A VICTIM'S FACE

In his deep dive into the dark world of serial killers, Clive crafted a chilling artifact for his workspace—a lampshade fashioned from the face of one of his first victims, Samantha White. The lamp cast an eerie pinky-beige light through Samantha's stretched cheeks and stitched eyelids, creating a macabre ambiance that symbolized the horrific blend of artistry and brutality that defines serial killers like Ed Gein. This grotesque creation served as a constant reminder of the fine line between craftsmanship and monstrosity.

85. ANSWER: B. THE DISAPPEARANCE OF HIS LAST VICTIM, ROBERT PIEST

Ed Gein's final arrest was triggered by the disappearance of his last known victim, fifteen-year-old Robert Piest. Robert had approached Gein seeking a job and never returned home, prompting his mother to file a missing person report. Police immediately suspected Gein and conducted a thorough search of his property, uncovering the remains of twenty-six victims buried beneath his house. This discovery led to Gein's arrest in 1978, his subsequent conviction, and his eventual execution in 1994.

86. ANSWER: C. BY PERFORMING AS A CLOWN AND INVOLVING THEM IN HIS ACT

John Wayne Gacy exploited his role as Pogo the Clown to gain the trust of his victims. He performed at children's parties, charity events, and other community gatherings, using this friendly and approachable persona to lure young boys and men into his home. Once inside, Gacy would trick his victims into wearing handcuffs under the pretense of performing a magic trick. This method allowed him to maintain control and distance while committing his heinous crimes, ultimately burying many of his victims beneath his house and shocking the community with the revelation of his true nature.

87. ANSWER: B. HE REVISITED AND ENGAGED WITH THEIR CORPSES

Ted Bundy's depraved nature extended beyond murder; he exhibited horrific behavior by revisiting and engaging with the corpses of his victims. Bundy would return to the bodies, raping and torturing them post-mortem, and sometimes keeping skulls as macabre trophies. His necrophilic actions highlighted the extreme depths of his psychopathy, as he derived a twisted sense of control and gratification from these interactions. Bundy's relentless pursuit of his victims, coupled with his brutal post-mortem activities, solidified his reputation as one of the most notorious and terrifying serial killers in history. Bundy was ultimately captured in 1978, sentenced to death, and executed in 1989 without ever showing remorse for his gruesome actions.

88. ANSWER: C. A PLUMBER FOUND HUMAN REMAINS IN A DRAIN

Dennis Nilsen, known for his sloppy disposal of bodies, was finally apprehended when a plumber discovered human remains clogging a communal drain. This careless mistake exposed his gruesome crimes, proving that even the most careful killers can be undone by their own negligence.

89. ANSWER: B. INTEGRATING MASONIC SYMBOLS

Clive's fascination with Jack the Ripper led him to incorporate Masonic symbols into his fictional murder reconstructions. This macabre detail underscores the intricate and ritualistic aspects that some serial killers bring to their crimes, adding a layer of dark symbolism to their heinous acts.

90. ANSWER : D. ITS UNIQUE AND TERRIFYING IMAGERY

Clive was particularly captivated by the nickname "The Killer Clown" because of its unique and horrifying imagery. The juxtaposition of a friendly, playful figure like a clown with the brutality of a serial killer creates a chilling and unforgettable moniker that embodies the essence of duality and deception.

91. ANSWER: C. SHE WAS TURNED ON BY PAUL'S ACTIONS

Karla Homolka, initially perceived as a kind and loving young woman, became deeply infatuated with her partner, Paul Bernardo. Unlike typical victims, Karla found herself aroused by Paul's violent tendencies. When Paul expressed a desire to kill her sister Tammy because she was a virgin, Karla willingly handed Tammy over. This disturbing act was driven by her obsession with Paul, leading to the tragic murder of her sister and two other young girls. Karla's participation in the crimes, including drugging and raping Tammy, highlighted the complex and manipulative dynamics of their relationship, ultimately resulting in her life sentence after confessing to the murders.

92. ANSWER: B. VIA LONELY HEARTS ADS

Martha Beck and Raymond Fernandez, known as the Lonely Hearts Killers, orchestrated their killing spree by responding to lonely hearts advertisements placed in newspapers. Raymond, a smooth talker, and Martha, posing as his sister, lured unsuspecting women seeking companionship. Their manipulative tactics allowed them to gain the trust of their victims, leading to abductions and murders across New York and Michigan. Their gruesome methods culminated in the murders of Daphne Downing and her two-year-old daughter, which eventually drew the attention of vigilant neighbors and law enforcement, leading to their arrest and conviction for three murders.

93. ANSWER: C. VIDEO RECORDINGS OF THE CRIMES

The Birnie murder spree was particularly heinous, involving the rape and murder of multiple women. A crucial piece of evidence that led to the Birnies' arrest was the discovery of video recordings. These tapes captured David Birnie raping and torturing their victims, including the tragic case of Denise Brown, who survived an initial attack but was ultimately killed. The existence of these recordings provided undeniable proof of their crimes, resulting in their sentencing to life in prison. David Birnie later took his own life, while Catherine Birnie remained incarcerated, never to be released.

94. ANSWER: C. TO PLAN REAL-LIFE REENACTMENTS OF SERIAL KILLINGS

Clive's involvement with the Thrill-Kill website went beyond mere fascination with serial killers. He used the platform to select notorious murderers and meticulously plan real-life reenactments of their crimes. By spinning the wheel of names like John Wayne Gacy and Dennis Nilsen, Clive sought to emulate their brutal methods, driven by an obsessive desire to reconstruct their heinous acts accurately. This disturbing behavior highlighted the dangerous allure of true crime to some individuals, blurring the lines between fascination and fanaticism.

95. ANSWER: B. VIA KATE MOIR'S ESCAPE AND POLICE REPORT

The Birnie couple's reign of terror came to an end when their sole survivor, Kate Moir, managed to escape their clutches. After being chained and raped, Kate was forced to call her parents to prevent suspicion. However, when Catherine Birnie stepped away to answer the doorbell, Kate seized the opportunity to flee through a window and seek help at a nearby grocery store. Her quick thinking and bravery led her to contact the police, who were then able to locate and arrest Catherine and David Birnie. This pivotal escape and subsequent police report were instrumental in uncovering the full extent of their brutal crimes.

96. ANSWER: B. LOVE VS. OBSESSION

Psychiatrists debated whether Catherine Birnie's participation in the murders was driven by genuine love or a twisted obsession with her partner, David Birnie. It was suggested that Catherine was so fixated on David that she was willing to commit heinous acts under his influence. This intense and unhealthy attachment blurred the lines between affection and compulsion, making it difficult to discern the true nature of her motivations. Her unwavering loyalty ultimately led her to partake in the rape and murder of several women, cementing her role in one of Australia's

97. ANSWER: C. SHE WAS RAISED IN AN INCESTUOUS HOUSEHOLD

Rosemary West's descent into serial killing was significantly influenced by her abusive upbringing. Growing up in an incestuous household, Rosemary experienced severe sexual abuse from her father and later from Fred West. These traumatic early experiences distorted her understanding of relationships and normal behavior, paving the way for her participation in the rape, torture, and murder of twelve girls and young women. Rosemary's background of abuse played a crucial role in shaping her violent tendencies and her willingness to collaborate with Fred West in their heinous crimes.

98. ANSWER: D. THE COUPLE'S ABILITY TO MANIPULATE AND CONCEAL EVIDENCE

Rosemary and Fred West were able to evade detection for years due to their meticulous efforts to manipulate and conceal evidence. They often moved their victims between different locations, making it difficult for authorities to connect the dots between the disappearances. Additionally, their use of torture and varied methods of disposal added layers of complexity to their crimes, preventing early identification and linking of the murders. Their strategic concealment of bodies in their garden ultimately led to their capture, but not before they had committed numerous atrocities.

99. ANSWER: B. DISCOVERY OF THEIR VICTIMS' REMAINS ON SADDLEWORTH MOOR

The arrest of Ian Brady and Myra Hindley, the Moors Murderers, was primarily due to the discovery of their victims' remains buried along Saddleworth Moor. This grim evidence provided the crucial link needed for law enforcement to convict the couple of their multiple murders. The extensive search and forensic investigation uncovered the bodies of several victims, which solidified the case against Brady and Hindley, leading to their life sentences and ensuring they would never harm another victim.

100. ANSWER: C. SEXUAL GRATIFICATION AND CONTROL

During their trial, Ian Brady and Myra Hindley primarily cited sexual gratification and a desire for control as their motivations for committing the Moors Murders. Their heinous acts were driven by a sadistic need to dominate and torture their victims, fulfilling their twisted desires. This combination of sexual violence and psychological control underscored the depth of their depravity, making their crimes some of the most brutal and shocking in British history.

101. ANSWER: B. A WORKER FOUND INFANT BODIES IN A CLOGGED DRAIN

Sarah and John Makin's dark secret was uncovered when a worker cleaning a clogged drain discovered the remains of two infants. This horrifying discovery prompted the police to investigate the Makins' previous residences, where they found twelve infant bodies buried in their homes. Their actions as baby farmers turned deadly when they began murdering the babies they were supposed to care for, leading to their arrest and subsequent sentencing—John being executed in 1893 and Sarah receiving a life sentence.

102. ANSWER: B. THRILL-SEEKING AND DOMINANCE

Debra Brown and Alton Coleman engaged in a brutal crime spree driven by thrill-seeking and a desire for dominance over their victims. Their partnership was marked by a master-slave dynamic, where Debra, with her low IQ and dependent personality, followed Alton's lead in committing seven rapes, eight murders, and fourteen armed robberies across the Midwest. Their sadistic methods involved befriending victims, regardless of age or gender, and using their combined power to exert control and inflict terror. Both were sentenced to death, with Alton executed in 2002 and Debra receiving a life sentence due to her diminished mental capacity.

103. ANSWER: B. THEY BRAGGED ABOUT THEIR CRIMES

Gwendolyn Graham and Catherine May Wood, who worked as nurse's aides at Alpine Manor nursing home, were infamous for openly bragging about their murders. After suffocating their patients for sexual gratification, they took personal items from their victims and flaunted their gruesome deeds to coworkers. Their lack of concern for secrecy and their brazen discussions about the murders ultimately led to their downfall when Rosemary Graham confessed to her ex-husband, prompting police investigations that uncovered multiple remains. Gwendolyn Graham received five life sentences, while Catherine May Wood was sentenced to a reduced term.

104. ANSWER: C. SHE DISAPPEARED AND WAS NEVER FOUND

Charmaine, the stepdaughter of Fred and Rosemary West, became one of their missing victims after enduring relentless physical abuse. Rosemary West was particularly harsh on Charmaine, leading to her eventual disappearance. Despite their attempts to cover up their crimes, Charmaine was never found, adding to the horror and mystery surrounding the Wests' extensive list of victims. Her disappearance remains one of the many tragic losses inflicted by the couple, highlighting their extreme brutality and the depth of their depravity.

105. ANSWER: C. SHE ACTIVELY PARTICIPATED IN THE RAPES AND MURDERS

Catherine Birnie was not merely an accomplice but an active participant in the Birnie murder spree. Alongside her partner, David Birnie, she lured women into their car, chained them to the bed, and watched as David raped and murdered them. Catherine's involvement went beyond passive complicity, as she assisted in the abductions and supported the violent actions of her partner. Their collaborative brutality resulted in the deaths of multiple women, cementing their place as one of Australia's most notorious serial killer couples.

106. ANSWER: D. BY USING A COMBINATION OF STRANGULATION AND BLUDGEONING

Fred and Rosemary West employed a dual method of strangulation and bludgeoning to ensure their victims were dead before disposing of them. After abducting and raping their victims, Fred would often strangle them with his bare hands or use blunt objects like hammers to inflict fatal injuries. This combination of methods made it certain that their victims were dead, allowing them to bury the remains in their garden or other concealed locations. Their ruthless approach to murder demonstrated their complete lack of empathy and the extent of their sadistic tendencies.

107. ANSWER: C. A FAILED ATTEMPT TO INVOLVE MYRA'S YOUNGER BROTHER

The final capture of Ian Brady and Myra Hindley occurred when they attempted to involve Myra's younger brother in their crimes. After murdering a young man, they tried to get him to help clean up the crime scene. However, the young man managed to escape and immediately contacted the police, leading to a thorough investigation. This failed attempt to implicate another individual exposed their murderous activities, resulting in their arrest and subsequent life sentences for their numerous heinous crimes.

108. ANSWER: B. HER LOW IQ AND DEPENDENT PERSONALITY

Debra Brown received a life sentence for her involvement in the crimes committed alongside Alton Coleman due to her low IQ and dependent personality. Her mental state made it difficult for her to fully comprehend the gravity of their actions, leading to a reduced sentence compared to Alton, who was executed in 2002. Debra's psychological condition played a significant role in her sentencing, highlighting how mental health factors can influence legal outcomes even in cases of severe criminal behavior.

109. ANSWER: C. BOTH WERE EQUALLY INVOLVED IN THE RAPES AND MURDERS

Gerald and Charlene Gallego were equally involved in their horrifying crimes. Gerald took the lead in raping and murdering their victims, while Charlene actively participated by driving the van and watching the atrocities unfold through the rearview mirror. Their collaborative approach made them a particularly dangerous and ruthless serial killer couple, responsible for the deaths of ten individuals in Sacramento, California. Their joint actions and lack of remorse highlighted the depths of their depravity, leading to their eventual sentencing—Gerald to death and Charlene receiving a reduced sentence for her cooperation.

110. ANSWER: B. DELFINA, MARIA, CARMEN, AND LUISA

Las Poquianchis were the de Jesús González sisters—Delfina, Maria, Carmen, and Luisa—infamous for running multiple brothels in Mexico during the 1950s and 1960s. Operating the notorious Rancho El Ángel, also known as the "Bordello from Hell," the sisters lured women under the guise of housekeeping jobs. Once trapped, the women were forced into drug addiction and prostitution. Victims deemed too old were brutally beaten and starved to death. Their reign of terror ended when a procurer was arrested and implicated them, leading to the discovery of numerous buried bodies on their property. The sisters received forty-year sentences each, marking them as some of Mexico's deadliest female serial killers.

111. ANSWER: B. MARY ANN COTTON

Mary Ann Cotton is recognized as Britain's first known serial killer, responsible for the deaths of at least twenty-one individuals to claim insurance money. Operating in the late 19th century, Cotton used arsenic—a common household poison at the time—to murder her victims, including three husbands, a friend, eleven children, and a lover. Her string of deaths initially sparked rumors of a curse, but a diligent doctor's investigation revealed high arsenic levels in the remains, leading to her conviction and execution for the murder of her stepson. Cotton's calculated use of poisoning for financial gain set a grim precedent in the annals of true crime.

112. ANSWER: C. EMPRESS CATHERINE II

Darya Nikolayevna Saltykova, a Russian aristocrat, was notorious for torturing and murdering over a hundred of her servants, predominantly young women. Her heinous acts remained unchecked due to her powerful connections within the Saltykova family. It wasn't until relentless petitions from the victims' relatives reached Empress Catherine II that a thorough investigation was launched. In 1762, Saltykova was arrested and linked to 138 suspicious deaths. Despite the abolishment of the death penalty in 1754, Catherine II sentenced her to life imprisonment, where she spent the remainder of her days in the basement of the Ivanovsky Convent, forever marked by her inhumane crimes.

113. ANSWER: B. MORE THAN 400

Amelia Dyer stands as one of Britain's most notorious serial killers, responsible for the deaths of over four hundred infants through the grim practice of baby farming. After her husband's death left her financially desperate, Dyer took in babies for a fee, only to starve, drug, or drown them in the River Thames. Her spree continued unchecked until the discovery of baby Helena Fry's remains led to her capture. The stench of decomposition at her residence further exposed her atrocities. Convicted for the murders of six infants, Dyer was sentenced to death and executed in 1896, leaving behind an indelible legacy of maternal cruelty.

114. ANSWER: B. POISONING WITH ARSENIC

Maria Catherina Swanenburg, driven by greed, became one of history's most prolific female serial killers in Britain. From 1880 to 1883, she poisoned at least twenty-seven people, primarily her parents, to secure their insurance and inheritances. Utilizing arsenic, readily available in household products like rat poison, Swanenburg meticulously moved between homes to avoid suspicion. Her scheme unraveled when a doctor discovered elevated arsenic levels in a victim's remains, leading to her arrest in 1883. Although suspected of over ninety murders, she was only convicted for three and sentenced to life imprisonment, highlighting the challenges of prosecuting female serial killers in that era.

115. ANSWER: B. A DETECTIVE LINKED HER TO MULTIPLE DEATHS THROUGH AUTOPSIES

Hélène Jégado, a charismatic Frenchwoman, was responsible for the deaths of at least thirty-six individuals over eighteen years, primarily using arsenic to poison her victims. Her spree began while working for a priest and continued through her employment with a law professor, where a series of unexplained deaths raised suspicions. A diligent detective ordered autopsies, revealing high arsenic levels that connected Jégado to the murders. Convicted of three murders and three attempted murders, she was executed in 1852. Jégado's ability to manipulate those around her and her calculated use of poison made her one of history's most sinister female serial killers.

116. ANSWER: B. ANYWHERE FROM ELEVEN TO FORTY-SIX

Genene Anne Jones, a pediatric nurse from Texas, is suspected of murdering between eleven and forty-six infants under her care. Driven by a twisted desire for attention and adoration, Jones administered lethal doses of heparin, digoxin, and succinylcholine to induce cardiac arrest in her young patients. Her actions went unnoticed for years as hospital records were destroyed to prevent lawsuits. It wasn't until she moved to Kerrville, Texas, and was caught poisoning six children that her gruesome spree was exposed. Convicted for the murders of Chelsea McClellan and Rolando Jones, Jones received ninety-nine and sixty-year sentences, respectively, ending her horrific acts.

117. ANSWER: C. HATRED FOR CHILDREN STEMMING FROM HER OWN NEGLECTED CHILDHOOD

Felícitas Sánchez developed a profound hatred for children due to her own lack of maternal love and neglect. Growing up without affection, she became psychopathic and despised all things maternal. Graduating as a nurse, Sánchez engaged in baby farming—handling, prostituting, and ultimately killing unwanted children. She disposed of the bodies by discarding them in sewers or incinerators. Her spree was halted in 1941 when remains were found near her residence, leading to her arrest.

Unable to withstand her crimes, Sánchez committed suicide three months after her capture, leaving behind a legacy of maternal cruelty and murder.

118. ANSWER: C. IAN BRADY AND MYRA HINDLEY

Ian Brady and Myra Hindley, infamously known as the Moors Murderers, terrorized the United Kingdom between 1963 and 1965 by abducting, torturing, and killing twelve girls and young women. Their crimes were marked by extreme violence and sadistic pleasure, with many victims buried along Saddleworth Moor. Their partnership was characterized by a dominant-submissive dynamic, with Brady orchestrating the murders and Hindley actively participating. They were ultimately caught after attempting to involve a young man in their crimes, leading to the discovery of their gruesome acts. Both were sentenced to life in prison, ensuring they would never harm another victim.

119. ANSWER: C. THEY KEPT THEIR VICTIMS AS SEX SLAVES BEFORE MURDERING THEM

Gerald and Charlene Gallego operated in Sacramento, California, from 1978 to 1980, brutally murdering ten people. The couple lured teenage girls into their van under false pretenses, with Charlene driving and Gerald raping the victims in the back. After extended periods of torture, they either shot or bludgeoned the girls to death, ensuring there was no chance of survival. Their horrific crimes were exposed when Gerald's careless disposal of bodies led to the discovery of multiple victims. Charlene testified against Gerald, receiving a sixteen-year sentence, while Gerald was sentenced to death. Their reign of terror is a chilling example of serial killer couples exploiting trust and inflicting unimaginable suffering.

120. ANSWER: C. ATE PARTS OF THEIR BODIES

Joachim Kroll, a notorious German serial killer active between 1955 and 1976, murdered up to fourteen people. His gruesome modus operandi involved not only killing his victims but also engaging in necrophilia and cannibalism. Kroll confessed to eating parts of his victims, rationalizing it as a way to save on grocery bills. His heinous crimes were ultimately uncovered when a neighbor reported a clogged toilet filled with human remains, leading to his arrest. Convicted of multiple murders, Kroll was sentenced to nine life terms and died of a heart attack in 1991.

121. ANSWER: B. A NEIGHBOR REPORTED A CLOGGED TOILET

Joachim Kroll was apprehended after Marion Ketter went missing. Police investigations led to a neighbor who noticed a clogged toilet and suspected foul play. When questioned, Kroll admitted the pipes were backed up with "guts," prompting officers to search his apartment. They discovered Marion's remains, leading to his swift arrest. Kroll's confession revealed additional murders he had committed, showcasing his lack of remorse and deranged nature.

122. ANSWER: C. HE BELIEVED IT GAVE HIM AN ORGASM

Andrei Chikatilo, a prolific Russian serial killer active from 1978 to 1990, found sexual gratification in stabbing his female victims. This twisted compulsion drove him to commit up to fifty murders, targeting women and children. Chikatilo's heinous acts were a blend of sexual violence and extreme brutality, making him one of the most feared criminals in Soviet history. He was captured in 1990 and executed by firing squad in 1994, leaving behind a legacy of unimaginable horror.

123. ANSWER: C. HE SAW THEM AS THE ONLY WAY TO SATISFY HIS URGES

Andrei Chikatilo rationalized his brutal murders by viewing them as the only means to achieve sexual satisfaction. His inability to control his violent impulses led him to commit heinous acts repeatedly, targeting the most vulnerable members of society. Chikatilo's twisted perception of his actions underscores the extreme psychological disturbances that can drive individuals to commit serial killings. His lack of remorse and justification for his crimes further cemented his reputation as one of history's most depraved killers.

124. ANSWER: B. RODNEY ALCALA

Rodney Alcala, infamously known as "The Dating Game Killer," secured a date with Cheryl Bradshaw on the popular TV show "The Dating Game" despite already having committed multiple murders. His charming and charismatic demeanor masked his dark nature, allowing him to deceive and manipulate his victims effortlessly. Alcala's participation in the show highlighted the terrifying reality that some serial killers can blend seamlessly into normal society, evading suspicion and continuing their crimes until finally apprehended in 1978.

125. ANSWER: C. HE ESCAPED DURING A POLICE VISIT

After committing his first known murder, Rodney Alcala managed to evade capture by escaping during a police visit. When officers arrived to investigate the disappearance of an eight-year-old girl, Alcala appeared at the door, naked and feigning innocence. As officers attempted to render aid to the barely breathing victim, Alcala broke free and fled the scene. This daring escape allowed him to continue his killing spree until his eventual arrest years later.

126. ANSWER: C. HIS ACCOMPLICE SHOT HIM AND CALLED THE POLICE

Dean Corll, known as the "Disco Daddy," was ultimately captured when one of his accomplices, Elmer Wayne Henley, shot him while Corll was committing rape and murder. Following the shooting, Henley called the police and turned himself in, providing the authorities with the evidence needed to apprehend Corll. This dramatic end to Corll's reign of terror revealed the extent of his sadistic crimes, which included the abduction, rape, and murder of over twenty-eight young boys in Houston between 1970 and 1973.

127. ANSWER: B. IAN BRADY AND MYRA HINDLEY, KNOWN FOR BURYING VICTIMS ON SADDLEWORTH MOOR

Ian Brady and Myra Hindley, infamously known as the Moors Murderers, committed a series of heinous crimes between 1963 and 1965 in the United Kingdom. Their murders, which involved the rape and torture of twelve girls and young women, were particularly notable for the burial of their victims along Saddleworth Moor. Their sadistic partnership and the sheer brutality of their acts left a lasting impact on British society, making them one of the most notorious serial killer couples in history. Both were sentenced to life in prison, with Brady expressing no remorse for his actions.

128. ANSWER: C. THEY DIED IN PRISON

Ray and Faye Copeland, the oldest couple ever sentenced to death in the United States, never faced execution. Ray died of natural causes while awaiting his execution, and Faye suffered a stroke and was released to a nursing home due to her failing health, where she died in 2003. Their death sentences were never carried out, ending their horrifying spree of murdering at least five drifters they lured under the guise of employment opportunities.

129. ANSWER: B. THEY KEPT THEM AS SEX SLAVES BEFORE MURDERING THEM

Gerald and Charlene Gallego operated in Sacramento, California, from 1978 to 1980, abducting teenage girls and keeping them as sex slaves in their van. Gerald would rape the girls while Charlene watched, escalating their abuse by taking victims back to their home for extended periods of torture. Their brutal method involved prolonged sexual violence before murdering the victims by shooting or bludgeoning them to death. The couple was eventually arrested, with Gerald receiving the death penalty and Charlene serving sixteen years after testifying against him. Their crimes remain some of the most heinous in American serial killer history.

130. ANSWER: B. DISSECTED AND CONSUMED THEIR FLESH

Joachim Kroll, a notorious German serial killer active between 1955 and 1976, engaged in the grotesque practice of having sex with his victims' bodies and then dismembering them for consumption. His twisted rationale for cannibalism was to save on grocery expenses, a macabre justification that underscores his severe psychological disturbances. Kroll's heinous acts were ultimately uncovered when a neighbor reported a clogged toilet filled with "guts," leading to his arrest. He confessed to numerous additional murders, was sentenced to nine life terms, and died of a heart attack in 1991.

131. ANSWER: C. A PLUMBER DISCOVERED HUMAN REMAINS IN A DRAIN

Joachim Kroll was apprehended when a plumber investigating a clogged toilet in his apartment uncovered human remains. This careless oversight exposed Kroll's gruesome activities, leading to his arrest. Unlike many serial killers who meticulously plan their crimes, Kroll's inability to effectively dispose of his victims' bodies highlighted his deranged nature. His confession revealed a string of unsolved murders, solidifying his place as one of Germany's most infamous serial killers.

132. ANSWER: B. ACHIEVING AN ORGASM

Andrei Chikatilo, a prolific Russian serial killer active from 1978 to 1990, confessed that stabbing his female victims was the only way he could achieve an orgasm. This disturbing admission reveals the extreme psychosexual motivations driving his violent actions. Chikatilo's spree, which resulted in the deaths of up to fifty women and children, was marked by both sexual assault and brutal murder, making him one of the most feared criminals in Soviet history. He was executed by firing squad in 1994.

133. ANSWER: D. 56

Andrei Chikatilo confessed to killing fifty-six individuals, although he was officially tried and convicted for fifty-three murders. His victims ranged from young girls to adult women, and his crimes were characterized by extreme brutality and sexual violence. Chikatilo's ability to evade capture for over a decade only added to his notoriety, making him one of Russia's most infamous serial killers. His execution in 1994 marked the end of a reign of terror that left deep scars in the communities he targeted.

134. ANSWER: C. THE DATING GAME

Rodney James Alcala, known as one of the most notorious serial killers, appeared on the popular TV show "The Dating Game" and won a date with Cheryl Bradshaw. This chilling fact underscores the deceptive nature of Alcala, who managed to conceal his violent tendencies behind a charming and charismatic facade. Despite his involvement in murders and being a registered sex offender, the lack of thorough screening on the show allowed him to participate, highlighting significant flaws in the program's vetting process. Alcala's participation remains a haunting example of how easily true evil can hide behind an amiable exterior.

135. ANSWER: B. AN ACCOMPLICE TURNED HIMSELF IN AND SHOT CORLL

Dean Corll, a German serial killer active in the early 1970s, was finally apprehended when one of his accomplices, Elmer Wayne Henley, turned against him. During a violent confrontation, Henley shot Corll multiple times while Corll was committing rape and murder. Henley then immediately called the police and confessed to his involvement, leading to Corll's arrest. This dramatic end to Corll's murderous spree revealed the depth of his depravity and the extent of his manipulative control over his accomplices, who were complicit in his horrific crimes.

136. ANSWER: B. HE WAS A SOLDIER WHO ALSO TORTURED AND MURDERED CHILDREN

Gilles de Rais, a companion of Joan of Arc and a celebrated soldier during the Hundred Years' War, led a secret life as a serial killer. Behind his heroic facade, he tortured and murdered numerous children, driven by dark obsessions and sadistic desires. De Rais's heinous acts included kidnapping children to satisfy his twisted needs, and his crimes went undetected for years due to his esteemed position and influence. His eventual confession, coerced under threat of torture, revealed the full extent of his monstrous behavior, making him one of history's earliest documented serial killers.

137. ANSWER: B. THE MONSTER OF THE ANDES

Pedro Lopez, often referred to as "The Monster of the Andes," is a serial killer responsible for the rape and murder of at least fifty-three young girls across Ecuador, Colombia, and Peru. His heinous crimes were characterized by extreme violence and a predilection for targeting vulnerable and trusting young girls. Despite numerous confessions, much of Lopez's reported activity remains unverified due to his history of abuse and manipulation. After being released from prison in 1998 for good behavior, his current whereabouts remain unknown, adding an eerie layer of uncertainty to his already terrifying legacy.

138. ANSWER: B. HE STRANGLED AND DISMEMBERED HER

Albert Fish, known as "The Brooklyn Vampire," confessed to the gruesome murder of ten-year-old Grace Budd, among other victims. Fish claimed to have strangled her and then dismembered her body to consume parts of it. His sadistic actions were driven by a complete lack of empathy and remorse, making him one of the most feared and reviled serial killers in American history. Fish's chilling letter to Grace's mother further exemplifies his twisted psyche, where he casually described the horrific details of his crimes, leaving an indelible mark of horror on true crime history.

139. ANSWER: B. HE SENT HER A DETAILED LETTER DESCRIBING HIS MURDERS

Albert Fish infamously taunted the mother of one of his victims, Grace Budd, by sending her a detailed and horrific letter describing the abduction, torture, and murder of her child. In the letter, Fish grotesquely elaborated on how he killed Grace, revealing his necrophilic tendencies and complete disregard for human life. This macabre correspondence not only terrorized Grace's family but also highlighted Fish's deranged nature and his need to dominate and control his victims and their loved ones through fear and intimidation.

140. ANSWER: B. SAID HANAI

Said Hanai earned the grim title of Iran's worst serial killer, confessing to the murders of approximately sixteen women in Mashhad between 2000 and 2001. Targeting prostitutes, Hanai viewed them as nuisances in his neighborhood and justified his killings as a religious duty to cleanse the area. His brutal method involved strangling victims with their headscarves and showing no remorse, referring to them as "worthless as cockroaches." Initially lauded by extremists for his actions, Hanai's heinous crimes were later exposed when it was revealed he had sexually abused thirteen of his victims before murdering them. Convicted and hanged in 2002, his legacy remains a dark chapter in Iran's criminal history.

141. ANSWER: C. HE HAD NO SPECIFIC VICTIM PROFILE AND KILLED FAR FROM HIS USUAL HAUNTS

Israel Keyes distinguished himself from other serial killers through his meticulous and unpredictable planning. Unlike many killers who have a specific victim profile, Keyes targeted individuals without any particular pattern, often killing far away from his home base to avoid detection. He employed strategic measures such as disabling his cell phone, using cash transactions, and preparing murder kits in advance to ensure his crimes remained untraceable. Keyes meticulously planned each murder, demonstrating a chilling level of control and foresight. His reign of terror ended when he committed suicide in his jail cell on December 2, 2012, leaving behind a legacy of fear and unanswered questions.

142. ANSWER: B. RANDY KRAFT

Randy Kraft, infamously dubbed the "Score Card Killer," terrorized the Los Angeles area during the 1980s by targeting young men, particularly Marines. Kraft maintained a coded notebook, or "score card," to keep track of his victims, reflecting his obsessive and organized nature. Preferring hitchhikers aged eighteen to twenty-five, he would abduct, sexually assault, and brutally strangle his victims, often using their belts as ligatures. Despite being linked to at least sixty deaths, only sixteen cases had sufficient evidence to convict him. Kraft's dual life as a soft-spoken computer programmer masked his monstrous activities, making him a particularly chilling figure in true crime history.

143. ANSWER: B. CHARLES WAS ARRESTED FOR SHOPLIFTING, LEADING TO THE DISCOVERY OF THEIR CRIMES

Charles Chi-Tat Ng and Leonard Lake operated as a deadly duo, responsible for at least eleven murders in California. Their capture was a result of Charles's kleptomania when he was arrested for shoplifting in 1985. This arrest led authorities to investigate further, uncovering their gruesome crimes. Leonard Lake, upon learning of Charles's capture, committed suicide by taking a cyanide capsule during interrogation. The subsequent police search of their ranch in Calaveras County revealed the remains of their victims, solidifying their infamy as one of America's most terrifying serial killer couples. Charles was later extradited and convicted of eleven murders, receiving a death sentence.

144. ANSWER: B. MIVACRON

Vickie Dawn Jackson, known as the "Angel of Death," utilized Mivacron, a powerful paralyzing drug, to murder her victims. Over the course of eleven days, she killed eight individuals at a small-town hospital where she worked as a nurse. Her victims, primarily patients recovering from surgeries or illnesses, were injected with Mivacron, causing them to stop breathing. Jackson's lack of remorse and the hospital's initial attempts to cover up the mysterious deaths highlighted the chilling efficiency of her method. Her spree went unnoticed until an investigation revealed the unnatural spike in patient deaths, leading to her arrest and conviction.

145. ANSWER: B. "WHAT TOOK YOU SO LONG?"

David Richard Berkowitz, infamously known as the Son of Sam, taunted authorities and the public with his heinous crimes in New York during the late 1970s. On August 10, 1977, Berkowitz was arrested after a woman reported seeing him remove a parking ticket from his yellow vehicle near one of the crime scenes. Upon his arrest, his first words were chillingly simple: "What took you so long?" This statement underscored his deranged mindset and lack of remorse for the random shootings that terrorized the city, leading to his conviction and six life sentences.

146. ANSWER: C. BEING OVERCONFIDENT AND MAKING A BRUTAL ERROR

The Birnie murder spree, perpetrated by Catherine and David Birnie, was ultimately halted by a critical mistake during one of their crimes. After brutally raping and stabbing Denise Brown, they believed she was dead and buried her in a shallow grave. However, Denise's survival instinct caused her to sit up, prompting David to strike her with an ax to ensure her death. This overconfident and brutal error left undeniable evidence of their crimes, leading to their swift arrest. The discovery of their signature brutal methods sealed their fate, resulting in life sentences for both, with David eventually committing suicide in prison.

147. ANSWER: B. OBSESSION AND LOYALTY TO DAVID

Psychiatrists analyzed Catherine Birnie's involvement in the horrific murders committed alongside her partner, David Birnie, and concluded that her actions were driven by an intense obsession and unwavering loyalty to him. Despite not having the inclination to kill on her own, Catherine was so fixated on David that she complied with his every demand, participating in the abductions, rapes, and murders. This deep-seated obsession underscored the psychological manipulation and control exerted by David, making Catherine an integral part of the Birnies' murderous spree.

148. ANSWER: B. THEY GREW UP IN VIOLENT, INCESTUOUS HOUSEHOLDS

Fred and Rosemary West's descent into serial killing was profoundly influenced by their traumatic childhoods. Fred West grew up in an incestuous environment where he was sexually abused by his parents, witnessing his father engaging in sexual acts with his sisters and enduring abuse from his mother starting at age twelve. Similarly, Rosemary Letts came from a background where incest was normalized, and she never saw anything wrong with it. These disturbing early experiences distorted their perceptions of normal relationships and consent, fueling their later actions of rape, torture, and murder. Their shared history of abuse created a toxic bond that enabled them to commit some of the most heinous crimes in British history.

149. ANSWER: B. INJECTION OF A PARALYZING DRUG

Vickie Dawn Jackson, dubbed the "Angel of Death," employed the paralyzing drug Mivacron to kill her victims swiftly and efficiently. By injecting this drug into her patients, she caused them to stop breathing, ensuring that they could not escape or resist her lethal intentions. Her method was both calculated and cold, allowing her to murder eight individuals within eleven days without immediate detection. The hospital initially failed to notice the pattern of deaths, highlighting the silent and methodical nature of her crimes until the horrifying truth came to light.

150. ANSWER: B. WILLIAM DEVIN HOWELL

William Devin Howell is recognized as the most prolific serial killer in Connecticut. Convicted of manslaughter, Howell confessed to the murders of six additional women and one man in 2003. All victims were discovered in the New Britain area, and Howell admitted that rape was his primary motive for killing. His brutal actions included strangling Danny Whistnant, who he murdered after discovering Danny's disguise. Howell's calm demeanor during interviews, where he casually discussed his crimes, highlighted his chilling lack of remorse. Despite his heinous acts, Howell did not attempt to conceal his identity, which ultimately led to his capture and conviction.

151. ANSWER: A. THE DISAPPEARANCE OF SHANNAN GILBERT

The disappearance of Shannan Gilbert was the catalyst for the extensive search for the Long Island Serial Killer. Shannan, a sex worker, vanished after leaving a client's house, leading to a frantic police investigation. Despite her prolonged call to 911, Shannan was never found. During the search, authorities discovered the remains of several other victims, including Melissa Barthelemy, Maureen Brainard, Megan Waterman, and Amber Costello, scattered along the Ocean Parkway. The case remains unsolved, with Rex Heuermann arrested in connection but yet to stand trial. The mystery surrounding the Long Island Serial Killer continues to intrigue and terrify investigators and true crime enthusiasts alike.

152. ANSWER: B. SKETCHING HIS VICTIMS

The Doodler, a serial killer active in San Francisco during the 1970s, earned his moniker by sketching his victims before murdering them. Targeting gay white men, the Doodler met his victims in or near gay clubs, capturing their likenesses through drawings. This unsettling behavior not only adds a layer of premeditation to his crimes but also serves as a chilling reminder of his methodical approach. Despite several assaults and murders, the Doodler was never caught, leaving his identity and motives shrouded in mystery. Advances in DNA technology may one day uncover the truth behind these brutal acts.

153. ANSWER: B. CLEVELAND, OHIO

The Cleveland Torso Killer, active in the 1930s, terrorized Cleveland, Ohio, by dismembering his victims and leaving their remains in public areas like Kingsbury Run. Targeting primarily vagrants and individuals on society's fringes, this unknown serial killer was responsible for the gruesome deaths of twelve people between

1935 and 1938. The brutality of the murders, involving decapitation and dismemberment, created a scene of horror and bloodshed. Despite numerous suspects, including Francis Sweeney, the Cleveland Torso Killer was never identified, leaving a legacy of fear and unanswered questions in Cleveland's history.

154. ANSWER: B. KILLING VICTIMS IN PAIRS WITHIN THEIR CARS

The Colonial Parkway Killer, active between 1986 and 1989 in South-East Virginia, was notorious for targeting couples sitting together in their cars. Unlike many serial killers who prefer solitary victims, this killer preferred attacking pairs, often while they were distracted or engaged in intimate moments. The murders involved various methods, including shooting, strangulation, and stabbing, and the killer would subsequently drive the victims' cars away from the crime scenes. The case remains unsolved, with theories suggesting the killer may have impersonated a police officer to gain control over his victims, but definitive evidence has yet to link any suspect to the heinous crimes.

155. ANSWER: B. THRILL-SEEKING AND OBSESSION WITH DEATH

Dr. Michael Swango, also known as "Dr. Death," was a serial killer who murdered up to fifty people through poisoning while working as a physician in the U.S. and Africa. Swango claimed his primary motivation was a twisted obsession with death and the thrill of killing. Unlike other serial killers driven by financial gain or revenge, Swango found satisfaction in the act of taking lives, often exhibiting a calm and nonchalant demeanor that allowed him to conceal his true nature. His crimes went undetected for years, highlighting the dangers posed by individuals in positions of trust and authority.

156. ANSWER: C. STABBING WITH AN AX

The Servant Girl Killer, active in Austin, Texas, during the late 1800s, was infamous for brutally murdering seven women with an ax. Targeting primarily black women and some white women, his method involved beating his victims to death outdoors, leaving their bodies in public spaces. The first victim, Mollie Smith, was found near an outhouse, while Grace Vance suffered such severe head trauma that her skull resembled jelly. Despite over four hundred suspects, including Nathan Elgin and Maurice, the Servant Girl Killer was never definitively identified, allowing the gruesome murders to remain unsolved and haunting the community.

157. ANSWER: C. DROVE THEM AWAY FROM THE LOCATION

The Colonial Parkway Killer, active in South-East Virginia from 1986 to 1989, had a distinctive method of handling his victims' vehicles by driving them away from the murder sites. This practice distinguished him from other serial killers who might abandon or destroy vehicles. By moving the cars, he attempted to obscure the crime scenes and reduce the likelihood of immediate discovery. The killer targeted young couples, often luring them into vulnerable situations before committing the murders. Despite extensive investigations, the Colonial Parkway Killer remains unidentified, adding to the enduring mystery and fear surrounding the case.

158. ANSWER: D. THE SERIAL KILLER COUPLE

Henry Lee Lucas and Ottis Elwood Toole are infamous as one of America's most notorious serial killer couples. Their partnership, which began in 1976, was marked by a sexual and criminal alliance, leading to the alleged murder of over a hundred people together. Their collaboration involved mutual influence and shared sadistic tendencies, making them a feared duo in the annals of true crime. Despite their numerous confessions, the veracity of their claims remains questionable due to their notorious dishonesty, but their combined legacy as serial killers endures as a chilling example of evil intertwined in partnership.

159. ANSWER: B. TEENAGE GIRLS THEY LURED INTO THEIR VAN FOR WORK

Gerald and Charlene Gallego, active in Sacramento, California, between 1978 and 1980, targeted teenage girls by luring them into their van under the guise of offering employment opportunities. Once inside, Gerald would rape the victims while Charlene watched, escalating to prolonged periods of abuse before ultimately murdering them by shooting or bludgeoning them. Their methodical approach involved keeping victims as sex slaves and ensuring their deaths were final and concealed. Gerald was sentenced to death, while Charlene received a sixteen-year sentence for her involvement, highlighting the couple's deeply depraved criminal partnership.

160. ANSWER: B. LAWRENCE BITTAKER AND ROY NORRIS

Lawrence Bittaker and Roy Norris, infamously known as the "Tool Box Killers," terrorized Southern California between June and October 1979. Operating from their van, aptly named the Murder Mack, they meticulously planned their abductions, targeting local girls on beaches. Their heinous acts involved raping and murdering five young women, all while recording their victims' screams. This gruesome practice not only heightened the horror of their crimes but also served as a macabre testament to their depravity. Their partnership was marked by equal participation in both rape and murder, making them one of the most terrifying serial killer duos in history.

161. ANSWER: C. FILLED THEIR CHEST CAVITIES WITH ROCKS AND PLACED THEM IN THE RIVER

The Harper brothers, Joshua ("Big") and William ("Wiley") Harper, were notorious serial killers in the late 1700s across Tennessee, Kentucky, and Illinois. Their sadistic methods went beyond mere murder; they mutilated their victims by cutting open their chest cavities, filling them with rocks, and then disposing of the bodies in rivers. This gruesome technique ensured that the bodies would sink, effectively concealing their crimes. Their extreme brutality and disregard for their victims' lives shocked even the river pirates of the time, making the Harper brothers some of the most depraved murderers of their era.

162. ANSWER: C. MURDER MACK

Lawrence Bittaker and Roy Norris operated their gruesome crimes from a specially modified van they named the Murder Mack. This vehicle was designed without windows in the back and featured a sliding door on the passenger side, allowing them to easily abduct their victims without being seen. The Murder Mack became a symbol of their reign of terror as they used it to lure, rape, and murder five young women in Southern California during 1979. The van's ominous presence and purpose played a crucial role in their ability to carry out their sadistic plans undetected for several months.

163. ANSWER: D. THRILL-SEEKING AND ENJOYMENT OF THE ACT

The Harper brothers, Joshua and William, exhibited a disturbing preference for killing more for the sheer thrill and enjoyment of the act rather than for financial gain. Their spree across Tennessee, Kentucky, and Illinois was driven by a deep-seated depravity and a desire to inflict pain and terror. This obsession with murder as a form of entertainment highlights the extreme sadism and lack of empathy that fueled their heinous actions, distinguishing them from other killers who might be motivated by financial or power-related reasons.

164. ANSWER: B. PRETENDING TO BE UNDERCOVER POLICE OFFICERS

Kenneth Bianchi and Angelo Buono, known as the Hillside Stranglers, employed deceptive tactics to lure their victims into their vehicle by masquerading as undercover police officers. They used fake badges to gain the trust of unsuspecting women and girls, convincing them that they were safe to enter the car. This ruse allowed them to abduct, rape, and murder several victims in the hills above Los Angeles between 1977 and 1978. Their ability to convincingly portray authority figures enabled them to carry out their crimes with relative impunity until their eventual capture.

165. ANSWER: B. CONFESSING TO ALL HIS CRIMES

Steven Gordon, along with Franc Cano, was responsible for the rape and murder of four women. Despite being on probation and wearing ankle monitors as registered sex offenders, they managed to continue their heinous crimes. The critical factor that led to Steven Gordon's life sentence was his confession to the murders. This admission of guilt provided the necessary evidence for the prosecution to secure a conviction, ensuring that Gordon would spend the rest of his life behind bars for his brutal actions.

166. ANSWER: C. BEAT HER UNTIL SHE REFUSED TO CRY

Rosemary West, alongside her husband Fred West, subjected their stepdaughter Charmaine to relentless physical abuse. In a particularly brutal act, Rosemary beat Charmaine until she refused to cry, demonstrating a chilling lack of empathy and an appetite for cruelty. This horrific treatment was part of a larger pattern of abuse and murder carried out by the Wests, who raped, tortured, and killed twelve girls and young women in Gloucester. Their sadistic methods and utter disregard for human life made them one of the most feared and reviled serial killer couples in history.

167. ANSWER: B. INCORPORATING MASONIC SYMBOLS

Clive, obsessed with accurately reconstructing the gruesome methods of serial killers, intended to integrate Masonic symbols into his reenactment of Jack the Ripper's murders. This macabre addition was meant to reflect the ritualistic and symbolic aspects of the Ripper's crimes, adding a layer of dark sophistication to his fictional portrayal. By embedding such sinister symbols, Clive aimed to deepen the authenticity and horror of his crime reenactments, highlighting his twisted fascination with the historical killer's methods.

168. ANSWER: B. THEY MURDERED FIVE DRIFTERS THEY HIRED

Ray and Faye Copeland earned notoriety as the oldest couple ever sentenced to death in the United States for the brutal murders of at least five drifters. Operating between 1968 and 1983, they lured their victims under the guise of employment opportunities. Once isolated in their van, Ray would brutally murder the men, while Faye's involvement remained ambiguous. A crucial piece of evidence—a list of victims' names marked with Xs in Faye's handwriting—suggested her complicity. Despite their death sentences, both Ray and Faye died in prison before their sentences could be carried out, Ray from natural causes and Faye from a stroke after being released to a nursing home due to her deteriorating health.

169. ANSWER: C. A SEXUAL RELATIONSHIP AND MUTUAL INFLUENCE

Ottis Elwood Toole and Henry Lee Lucas formed a deadly partnership that fueled one of the most extensive serial killing sprees in American history. Meeting in 1976, their relationship was both sexual and criminal, with each man influencing the other's violent tendencies. Together, they allegedly murdered over a hundred people, though much of their collaboration remains unverified due to their notorious dishonesty. Their twisted bond and mutual encouragement in their crimes made them one of the most feared serial killer duos, leaving a trail of terror and unanswered questions in their wake.

170. ANSWER: C. THEY KEPT VICTIMS AS SEX SLAVES BEFORE MURDERING THEM

Gerald and Charlene Gallego terrorized Sacramento, California, from 1978 to 1980 by abducting teenage girls and keeping them as sex slaves in their van. Gerald would rape the girls in the back while Charlene watched through the rearview mirror. On occasion, they took victims back to their home, where Gerald would subject them to hours of rape before murdering them by shooting or beating them to death. Their especially brutal method was highlighted when Gerald killed a victim named Kippi Vaught by repeatedly shooting her in the head after noticing she was still alive. Their reign of terror ended when they were arrested, with Gerald receiving a death sentence and Charlene testifying against him, earning sixteen years in prison.

171. ANSWER: C. DISCOVERY OF BODIES IN THEIR GARDEN

Ian Brady and Myra Hindley were ultimately apprehended when police obtained a search warrant for their home, leading to the discovery of multiple victims' remains buried in their garden. This gruesome find provided irrefutable evidence of their murderous spree, known as the Moors Murders, where they abducted, tortured, and killed twelve girls and young women between 1963 and 1965. The unearthing of these bodies along Saddleworth Moor sealed their fate, resulting in life sentences for both perpetrators and ending one of the most horrifying serial killing sprees in British history.

172. ANSWER: C. ITS UNIQUE AND TERRIFYING IMAGERY

Clive was particularly captivated by the nickname "The Killer Clown" given to John Wayne Gacy. He admired how the juxtaposition of a seemingly innocent and joyful figure like a clown with the brutal reality of a serial killer created a unique and terrifying image. This macabre combination not only made Gacy's crimes more shocking but also highlighted the deceptive nature of serial killers who hide their true intentions behind a friendly facade. Clive found this imagery compelling, adding to his obsession with accurately reenacting Gacy's horrific methods.

173. ANSWER: B. THEY WERE CAUGHT DUE TO FAULTY ANKLE MONITORS

Steven Gordon and Franc Cano, both registered sex offenders on probation and wearing ankle monitors, continued their heinous crimes by raping and murdering four women. Their criminal spree was eventually halted when law enforcement linked the ankle monitors to the last known locations of their victims. This crucial connection enabled the police to track them down, leading to their arrest. While Jarrae Estepp was found dead in a recycling plant in 2014, three other victims remain missing. Steven Gordon was sentenced to death, while Franc Cano received a life sentence for his involvement in the murders.

174. ANSWER: C. THEY KILLED BABIES THEY WERE SUPPOSED TO CARE FOR

Amelia Sach and Annie Walters, known as the Finchley Baby Farmers, perpetrated some of the most disturbing crimes by killing babies entrusted to their care. Operating under the guise of a "lying-in" home where expectant mothers could leave their newborns for adoption, they instead poisoned the infants to eliminate them. Their heinous actions were uncovered when Annie's landlord, a police officer, grew suspicious of the increasing number of babies and began an investigation. The discovery of the murders highlighted the absolute depravity of using children as commodities for financial gain, leading to their execution and burial in unmarked graves.

175. ANSWER: B. THEY LURED TRAVELERS TO BLUFFS AND SHOVED THEM OFF

The Harper brothers, Joshua ("Big") and William ("Wiley"), shocked river pirates and communities alike with their brutal method of luring travelers to high bluffs, forcing them to strip naked, and then pushing them off the edge. This gruesome technique was both sadistic and highly effective, ensuring the complete disappearance of their victims. Their reign of terror across Tennessee, Kentucky, and Illinois during the late 1700s left a legacy of fear and disgust, marking them as some of the most depraved serial killers of their time.

176. ANSWER: B. THEY PERFORMED A TEST RUN BY PICKING UP LOCAL GIRLS AND TAKING THEIR PICTURES

Before embarking on their murderous spree, Lawrence Bittaker and Roy Norris conducted a disturbing test run to evaluate the ease of luring local girls. They frequented beaches, engaging with young women and convincing them to take pictures with them. This unsettling practice helped them gauge their ability to attract victims, ultimately leading to their decision to commit the brutal rapes and murders of five young women between June and October 1979. Their meticulous planning and chilling execution underscored their sadistic nature and lack of empathy.

177. ANSWER: C. MOSES STEGALL ATTACKED BIG HARPER

The Harper brothers, Joshua ("Big") and William ("Wiley"), were finally apprehended after Moses Stegall, a member of a posse chasing them, attacked Big Harper by cutting off his head while he was still conscious. This grisly act led to the discovery of Big Harper's severed head, prompting authorities to intensify their search. The gruesome evidence found by the posse underscored the brothers' extreme brutality and ultimately led to Wiley Harper's capture and execution, ending their spree of terror across the American frontier.

178. ANSWER: C. SHE WAS GIVEN PAPERS STATING SHE WOULD NEVER GET OUT

Rosemary West was sentenced to life in prison for her role in the abduction, rape, and murder of twelve girls and young women alongside her husband, Fred West. In a landmark decision, she became the second woman in Australian history to receive official papers stating she would never be released from prison. This permanent denial of parole ensured that Rosemary West would spend the rest of her life incarcerated, reflecting the severity and brutality of her crimes and the justice system's determination to keep her behind bars indefinitely.

179. ANSWER: B. THEY KILLED TRAVELERS AND LURED THEM TO BLUFFS

The Harper brothers, Joshua ("Big") and William ("Wiley"), incensed everyone they encountered by luring unsuspecting travelers to high bluffs, forcing them to strip naked, and then pushing them off to their deaths. Their relentless and sadistic method of murder not only shocked river pirates but also horrified entire communities across Tennessee, Kentucky, and Illinois. Their blatant cruelty and lack of remorse made them universally despised and feared, ensuring that their names became synonymous with terror and depravity in the regions they terrorized.

180. ANSWER: C. RAYA AND SAKINA

Raya and Sakina were pioneering female serial killers in early 20th-century Alexandria, Egypt. Alongside their husbands and two other men, they orchestrated the disappearance and brutal murder of at least seventeen women. Targeting women who wore excessive jewelry and carried significant amounts of money, the sisters managed a brothel to lure their victims. Their method involved intoxicating their targets with alcohol, then suffocating them with a wet cloth. Their gruesome spree culminated in the discovery of dismembered bodies and led to their execution, marking a dark chapter in Egypt's criminal history.

181. ANSWER: C. SHE SAT UP IN HER GRAVE

Denise Brown, a 21-year-old victim of Catherine and David Birnie, narrowly escaped death after being brutally raped and stabbed. Believing she was dead, the Birnies buried her in a shallow grave. However, Denise's survival instincts kicked in, causing her to sit up despite the knife wound in her neck. Panicked, David Birnie struck her with an ax twice to ensure her demise before burying her again. This horrifying incident showcased the Birnies' relentless and sadistic nature, ultimately leading to their capture when their pattern of gruesome murders became apparent.

182. ANSWER: C. JOHN DUFFY CONFESSED AFTER TEN YEARS

John Duffy and David Mulcahy, known as the Railway Killers, embarked on a violent spree starting in 1982, assaulting over twenty women near railway stations. Their friendship, rooted in childhood, took a dark turn when they began their murders in 1985. Despite Duffy's prior conviction as a sex offender and his work as a railroad carpenter, it wasn't until a decade later that he confessed to the murders, implicating Mulcahy through DNA evidence. This confession brought an end to their reign of terror, highlighting the persistent dangers posed by serial killers and the importance of forensic advancements in solving such cases.

183. ANSWER: C. 15 YEARS

Loren Herzog and Wesley Shermantine, infamously dubbed the Speed Freak Killers, conducted a horrifying fifteen-year killing spree, responsible for the deaths of at least seventy individuals. Their partnership began in childhood, leading them to kill both together and separately. Fueled by methamphetamine addiction, their brutal methods raised questions about the role of substance abuse in driving serial killers. Their final victim, Cyndi Vanderheiden, was murdered in 1999, leading to their arrest and conviction in 2001. Herzog was paroled in 2010 but tragically committed suicide in 2012, while Shermantine remains on death row, reflecting the enduring impact of their crimes.

184. ANSWER: C. BEATING HER UNTIL SHE REFUSED TO CRY

Fred West, alongside his wife Rosemary, committed numerous heinous crimes, including the brutal abuse of his stepdaughter Charmaine. Fred subjected Charmaine to relentless physical violence, beating her until she stopped crying—a testament to his sadistic nature. This extreme form of abuse was part of a larger pattern of rape, torture, and murder perpetrated by the Wests, resulting in the deaths of twelve girls and young women. Their crimes remained hidden until the discovery of multiple bodies buried in their garden, leading to their arrest and life sentences, with Fred ultimately taking his own life in prison.

185. ANSWER: B. IAN BRADY AND MYRA HINDLEY

Ian Brady and Myra Hindley, infamously known as the Moors Murderers, terrorized the United Kingdom between 1963 and 1965 by abducting, torturing, and murdering twelve girls and young women. Their victims were often buried along

Saddleworth Moor, giving the murders their infamous name. Brady's troubled childhood and Hindley's manipulation created a lethal partnership marked by extreme violence and depravity. Their eventual capture was triggered by an unsuccessful attempt to involve Hindley's younger brother, leading to the discovery of multiple bodies and their subsequent life sentences in prison.

186. ANSWER: B. THEY MURDERED FIVE DRIFTERS THEY HIRED

Ray and Faye Copeland became the oldest couple ever sentenced to death in the United States for the murders of at least five drifters. Operating between 1968 and 1983, they lured their victims under the guise of employment opportunities. Ray brutally killed the men when they were no longer needed, while Faye's involvement was questioned through a list of victims marked with Xs in her handwriting. Despite Ray's indifference towards his death sentence and Faye's eventual release to a nursing home due to poor health, both died before their sentences could be executed, marking a grim end to their murderous spree.

187. ANSWER: B. THEY ENGAGED IN A SEXUAL RELATIONSHIP WHILE KILLING TOGETHER

Ottis Elwood Toole and Henry Lee Lucas formed a notorious serial killer duo, believed to have murdered over a hundred people together. Meeting in Jacksonville, Florida, in 1976, their relationship was both sexual and criminal, with both men influencing each other's violent tendencies. Despite their numerous confessions, the truth behind their collaboration remains murky due to their extensive dishonesty. Whether they were responsible for all the murders they claimed or exaggerated their involvement, Toole and Lucas left a legacy of fear and mystery in American criminal history.

188. ANSWER: C. SHE BEAT HER UNTIL SHE REFUSED TO CRY

Rosemary West, in collaboration with her husband Fred West, perpetrated some of the most gruesome crimes in British history. Among their victims was Charmaine, Fred's stepdaughter, whom Rosemary brutally beat until she stopped crying. This extreme violence was part of a broader pattern of abuse and murder that resulted in the deaths of twelve girls and young women. The Wests' crimes were eventually uncovered when authorities discovered multiple bodies buried in their garden, leading to their arrest and life sentences. Rosemary's sadistic actions on Charmaine exemplify the depths of her depravity and complicity in the Wests' murderous spree.

189. ANSWER: C. "HURRY IT UP, YOU HOOSIER BASTARD! I COULD HANG A DOZEN MEN WHILE YOU'RE SCREWING AROUND!"

Carl Panzram, a notorious American serial killer, expressed his defiance and aggression in his final moments with the chilling words, "Hurry it up, you Hoosier bastard! I could hang a dozen men while you're screwing around!" These last words encapsulate his ruthless nature and contempt for authority, leaving a lasting impression of his violent legacy.

190. ANSWER: C. PETER KÜRTEN

Peter Kürten, known as the Vampire of Düsseldorf, posed a haunting question before his execution: "Tell me. After my head has been chopped off, will I still be able to hear, at least for a moment, the sound of my own blood gushing from the stump of my neck? That would be a pleasure to end all pleasures." This macabre curiosity underscores his depraved fascination with death and his grotesque obsession with blood.

191. ANSWER: A. AMELIA DYER

Amelia Dyer, a British serial killer responsible for the deaths of numerous infants through infanticide, chose silence in her final moments with the words, "I have nothing to say." Her lack of remorse or final statement adds a chilling layer to her already horrifying crimes.

192. ANSWER: B. "TURN UP THE RADIO AND I'LL GO QUIETLY."

Peter Manuel, one of Britain's most feared serial killers, requested a peaceful end to his life with the words, "Turn up the radio and I'll go quietly." This calm and controlled statement starkly contrasts the brutality of his crimes, highlighting his desire for a serene final moment.

193. ANSWER: C. "I'D LIKE YOU TO GIVE MY LOVE TO MY FAMILY AND FRIENDS."

Ted Bundy, the charismatic and manipulative serial killer, chose to express love and concern for his family in his final words: “I’d like you to give my love to my family and friends.” This statement reveals a complex side of Bundy, juxtaposing his heinous actions with a seemingly affectionate farewell.

194. ANSWER: C. “KISS MY ASS.”

John Wayne Gacy, infamously known as "The Killer Clown," ended his life with a defiant and disrespectful remark: “Kiss my ass.” This statement epitomizes his brazen and unapologetic demeanor, even in the face of justice and impending death.

195. ANSWER: B. “I DON’T CARE IF I LIVE OR DIE. GO AHEAD AND KILL ME.”

Jeffrey Dahmer, the Milwaukee Cannibal, expressed complete indifference towards his fate with the words, “I don’t care if I live or die. Go ahead and kill me.” This apathetic farewell reflects his detached state of mind despite the gruesome nature of his crimes.

196. ANSWER: B. “I WOULD SUGGEST THAT WHEN A PERSON HAS A THOUGHT OF DOING ANYTHING SERIOUS AGAINST THE LAW, THAT BEFORE THEY DID THAT THEY SHOULD GO TO A QUIET PLACE AND THINK ABOUT IT SERIOUSLY.”

William Bonin, known as the Freeway Killer, used his final moments to impart a cautionary message: “I would suggest that when a person has a thought of doing anything serious against the law, that before they did that they should go to a quiet place and think about it seriously.” This ironic advice from a serial killer underscores the twisted logic often found in the minds of such criminals.

197. ANSWER: C. “I DON’T EVEN KNOW WHY I’M HERE.”

Albert Fish, the Brooklyn Vampire, left his final moments shrouded in confusion and detachment with the words, “I don’t even know why I’m here.” This perplexing statement adds to the eerie aura surrounding his already grotesque criminal legacy.

198. ANSWER: C. “I WANT TO ASK IF IT IS IN YOUR HEART TO FORGIVE ME.”

Angel Maturino Resendiz, known as the Railroad Killer, sought forgiveness in his last words: “I want to ask if it is in your heart to forgive me. You don't have to. I know I allowed the devil to rule my life. I just ask you to forgive me and ask the Lord to forgive me for allowing the devil to deceive me. I thank God for having patience in me. You did not deserve this. I deserve what I am getting.” This plea for forgiveness reveals a complex mix of remorse and resignation amidst his horrific actions.

199. ANSWER: B. “I REPENT, BUT I DO NOT FEAR DEATH.”

Fritz Haarmann, the Butcher of Hanover, conveyed a sense of repentance yet fearlessness towards his impending execution with the words, “I repent, but I do not fear death.” This declaration highlights the duality of remorse and the cold acceptance of his fate, encapsulating his troubled psyche.

200. ANSWER: D. “I’LL LET MY LAWYERS TALK FOR ME. I’M READY TO GO.”

Donald Henry Gaskins, an American serial killer, opted to delegate his final statements to his legal representation with the words, “I’ll let my lawyers talk for me. I’m ready to go.” This choice reflects his detached and resigned attitude towards his execution, leaving no personal message behind.

201. ANSWER: B. “I WANT TO SHOUT IT OUT, I LOVE MARTHA! WHAT DO THE PUBLIC KNOW ABOUT LOVE?”

Raymond Fernandez, part of the infamous "Lonely Hearts Killers," expressed his love and confusion about public perception with the words, “I want to shout it out, I love Martha! What do the public know about love?” This heartfelt yet disturbing farewell underscores the twisted nature of his criminal relationship and his inability to reconcile his violent actions with genuine emotions.

202. ANSWER: B. “MY STORY IS A LOVE STORY. BUT ONLY THOSE TORTURED BY LOVE CAN KNOW WHAT I MEAN... IMPRISONMENT IN THE DEATH HOUSE HAS ONLY STRENGTHENED MY FEELINGS FOR RAYMOND...”

Martha Beck, co-conspirator in the "Lonely Hearts Killers" duo, shared a deeply disturbing sentiment in her final words: “My story is a love story. But only those tortured by love can know what I mean... Imprisonment in the Death House has only strengthened my feelings for Raymond...” This declaration reveals the twisted and obsessive nature of her relationship with Raymond Fernandez, blurring the lines between love and madness.

203. ANSWER: C. "I'M GOING HOME, BABE."

Earle Nelson, known as the "Railroad Killer," ended his life with the unassuming yet eerie farewell, "I'm going home, babe." This casual statement belies the gruesome nature of his crimes, highlighting the stark contrast between his final words and his violent legacy.

204. ANSWER: C. "I WANT TO ASK IF IT IS IN YOUR HEART TO FORGIVE ME. YOU DON'T HAVE TO. I KNOW I ALLOWED THE DEVIL TO RULE MY LIFE. I JUST ASK YOU TO FORGIVE ME AND ASK THE LORD TO FORGIVE ME FOR ALLOWING THE DEVIL TO DECEIVE ME. I THANK GOD FOR HAVING PATIENCE IN ME. YOU DID NOT DESERVE THIS. I DESERVE WHAT I AM GETTING."

Angel Maturino Resendiz, known for his brutal crimes, expressed a profound plea for forgiveness in his final words: "I want to ask if it is in your heart to forgive me. You don't have to. I know I allowed the devil to rule my life. I just ask you to forgive me and ask the Lord to forgive me for allowing the devil to deceive me. I thank God for having patience in me. You did not deserve this. I deserve what I am getting." This heartfelt apology underscores the complex emotions and possible remorse behind his heinous actions.

205. ANSWER: B. "I REPENT, BUT I DO NOT FEAR DEATH."

Fritz Haarmann, infamously known as the Butcher of Hanover, expressed a conflicted state of mind in his final words: "I repent, but I do not fear death." This statement reveals his acknowledgment of wrongdoing yet a fearless acceptance of his fate, adding a layer of complexity to his already horrifying criminal persona.

206. ANSWER: D. "I'LL LET MY LAWYERS TALK FOR ME. I'M READY TO GO."

Donald Henry Gaskins, a prolific serial killer, chose to delegate his final statement to his legal team with the words, "I'll let my lawyers talk for me. I'm ready to go." This resignation and reliance on his attorneys reflect his detached and unrepentant attitude towards his impending execution.

207. ANSWER: D. "GENTLEMEN, I HAVE ONE LAST PIECE OF ADVICE: LOOK AWAY. THIS WILL NOT BE PRETTY TO SEE."

Marcel Petiot, a French doctor and serial killer, concluded his final moments with a menacing piece of advice: "Gentlemen, I have one last piece of advice: Look away. This will not be pretty to see." This ominous statement hinted at the gruesome nature of his crimes, leaving a lasting impression of his sinister character.

208. ANSWER: B. "LOOK AWAY. THIS WILL NOT BE PRETTY TO SEE."

Francis Crowely, a lesser-known serial killer, chose to warn those around him with the chilling words, "Look away. This will not be pretty to see." This foreboding statement served as a grim prelude to his execution, reflecting the dark nature of his crimes and his awareness of the horror he had inflicted on his victims.

209. ANSWER: C. [HEATHER WEST DID NOT HAVE RECORDED LAST WORDS]

Heather West, the daughter of Fred and Rosemary West, was brutally abused and ultimately disappeared under their horrific reign. There are no recorded last words from Heather, as her fate remains one of the darkest mysteries linked to the Wests' murderous spree.

210. ANSWER: B. "I DON'T EVEN KNOW WHY I'M HERE."

Frank Hunter, another serial killer, expressed bewilderment and detachment in his final moments with the statement, "I don't even know why I'm here." This perplexing remark adds to the eerie persona that surrounded his gruesome crimes and untimely death.

211. ANSWER: C. SHE DISAPPEARED WITHOUT A TRACE

Heather West, the youngest victim of Fred and Rosemary West, disappeared after enduring years of brutal abuse. Her disappearance remains one of the most haunting aspects of the Wests' crimes, with her fate still unknown, adding to the grim legacy of their murderous spree.

212. ANSWER: C. "I REPENT, BUT I DO NOT FEAR DEATH."

Fritz Haarmann, known as the Butcher of Hanover, conveyed a conflicted emotion in his last words: "I repent, but I do not fear death." This statement highlights his complex feelings of remorse intertwined with a fearless acceptance of his fate, deepening the eerie aura surrounding his gruesome crimes.

213. ANSWER: C. "I DON'T EVEN KNOW WHY I'M HERE."

Albert Fish, a sadistic serial killer, concluded his final moments with the perplexing and eerie statement, "I don't even know why I'm here." This baffling remark adds to the unsettling nature of his crimes, reflecting his disturbed mind and lack of remorse.

214. ANSWER: C. "I WANT TO ASK IF IT IS IN YOUR HEART TO FORGIVE ME. YOU DON'T HAVE TO. I KNOW I ALLOWED THE DEVIL TO RULE MY LIFE. I JUST ASK YOU TO FORGIVE ME AND ASK THE LORD TO FORGIVE ME FOR ALLOWING THE DEVIL TO DECEIVE ME. I THANK GOD FOR HAVING PATIENCE IN ME. YOU DID NOT DESERVE THIS. I DESERVE WHAT I AM GETTING."

Angel Maturino Resendiz, the Railroad Killer, conveyed a profound plea for forgiveness in his final words: "I want to ask if it is in your heart to forgive me. You don't have to. I know I allowed the devil to rule my life. I just ask you to forgive me and ask the Lord to forgive me for allowing the devil to deceive me. I thank God for having patience in me. You did not deserve this. I deserve what I am getting." This heartfelt apology provides a glimpse into his tortured psyche amidst his violent crimes.

215. ANSWER: B. THE BLACK DAHLIA

Elizabeth Short, famously known as the Black Dahlia, became the center of one of the most notorious cold cases in history after her mutilated body was discovered in 1947. Found sliced in half with minimal blood at the scene, her gruesome dismemberment baffled investigators. Despite numerous theories and extensive investigations, the true identity of her killer remains unknown, making the Black Dahlia case a lasting mystery that continues to fascinate true crime enthusiasts worldwide.

216. ANSWER: B. SIX YEARS OLD

JonBenet Ramsey, a six-year-old beauty queen, was tragically found dead in the basement of her Colorado home on December 26, 1996. The discovery was accompanied by a ransom note demanding $118,000 for her safe return. Despite intense media scrutiny and numerous theories implicating her family, the case remains unsolved. Critical missteps in the police investigation and the enduring mystery of the DNA evidence have kept JonBenet's murder one of the most enduring and debated cold cases in true crime history.

217. ANSWER: B. HER BELONGINGS WERE METICULOUSLY BURNED

On November 29, 1970, the charred remains of a woman were discovered in the Isdalen Valley of Norway. Known as the Isdal Woman, her body was burned beyond recognition, and all identifiable labels on her clothing and possessions had been removed. Authorities found two suitcases with items from various countries, suggesting she might have been a spy during the Cold War. Despite extensive investigations, the true identity and circumstances surrounding her death remain unresolved, adding to the eerie allure of the case.

218. ANSWER: B. LISTEN TO JAZZ MUSIC

The Axeman of New Orleans terrorized the city from 1918 to 1940, sending taunting letters to newspapers and threatening further killings unless residents played jazz music in their homes. This bizarre demand aimed to protect the populace from his violent rampages, during which he primarily targeted women and rarely men who intervened. Despite widespread fear and numerous victims, the Axeman was never caught, leaving his true identity a lingering mystery that continues to intrigue true crime aficionados.

219. ANSWER: A. JAMES LEWIS

In the 1982 Tylenol murders, seven people in the Chicago area died after consuming cyanide-laced Tylenol capsules. James Lewis was convicted of attempted extortion after sending a letter to Johnson & Johnson demanding $100,000 to stop the killings. While he was not directly linked to the actual poisonings, his suspicious actions and motive for revenge against the company led authorities to consider him a primary suspect. Despite his conviction, the true perpetrator of the Tylenol murders was never definitively identified, leaving the case unresolved.

220. ANSWER: C. TO ASSIST IN THE IMMEDIATE SEARCH FOR ABDUCTED CHILDREN

The Amber Alert system was created in response to the tragic abduction of nine-year-old Amber Hagerman in 1996. When Amber was kidnapped from a grocery store parking lot in Arlington, Texas, a witness named James Kevil called the police, but Amber was found four days later. The system was established to rapidly disseminate information about child abductions to the public, increasing the chances of rescuing missing children quickly. Today, Amber Alerts are a crucial tool in protecting children and aiding in their swift recovery.

221. ANSWER: B. HE SENT CRYPTIC LETTERS AND CIPHERS TO NEWSPAPERS

The Zodiac Killer is one of the most enigmatic and infamous serial killers, known not only for his brutal murders in the San Francisco area between 1968 and 1969 but also for his taunting letters and ciphers sent to newspapers. Claiming responsibility for at least five murders and possibly more, he engaged in a sinister game of cat and mouse with law enforcement, providing cryptic clues about his identity. Despite extensive investigations and numerous suspects, the Zodiac Killer was never caught, leaving his true identity and motives a lasting mystery.

222. ANSWER: C. SEALING ONLY HER BEDROOM INSTEAD OF THE ENTIRE HOUSE

In the investigation of JonBenet Ramsey's murder, police made a significant error by sealing off only her bedroom rather than treating the entire house as a crime scene. This oversight allowed friends and family members to remain present, compromising evidence and hindering the investigation. These mistakes fueled numerous theories and suspicions within the Ramsey family, contributing to the enduring mystery and lack of resolution in one of the most high-profile cold cases in true crime history.

223. ANSWER: C. HE SKETCHED HOW THE KILLER TAMPERED WITH THE BOTTLES

After being convicted of attempted extortion in connection with the Tylenol murders, James Lewis claimed he could assist authorities by sketching how the perpetrator might have tampered with the Tylenol bottles. Despite his offer, the FBI never conclusively linked Lewis to the actual poisonings, and the true culprit behind the deadly cyanide-laced capsules was never identified. Lewis maintained his innocence until his death, leaving the Tylenol murders as one of the most perplexing and unresolved cases in true crime history.

224. ANSWER: C. THE MOTIVE AND PERPETRATOR REMAIN UNKNOWN

The Gatton murders, which occurred in 1898, remain one of Australia's most baffling and eerie cases. Michael Murphy and his sisters, Ellen and Norah, were brutally murdered near Gatton while returning to their parents' farm. Despite a five-month investigation, no one was ever arrested, leading to widespread speculation about a possible coverup. The sole suspect, Theo Farmer, tragically took his own life in 1900, and the case remains unsolved to this day, partly due to the lack of forensic technology and the contamination of the crime scene by onlookers.

225. ANSWER: C. HE LIVED THIRTY-FIVE MINUTES AWAY FROM WHERE HER BODY WAS FOUND

Rahway Jane Doe, a young woman murdered in 1887 in Rahway, New Jersey, remains unidentified. The crime is particularly intriguing because Francis Tumblety, a suspect often associated with Jack the Ripper, was living in New York at the time—just thirty-five minutes away from the murder location. This proximity has led many to speculate about his potential involvement, although no definitive evidence has ever linked him to the case, leaving Rahway Jane Doe's killer still at large.

226. ANSWER: C. THE MARY ROGERS MURDER

The tragic case of Mary Rogers, who was murdered in 1841 after disappearing while visiting relatives, deeply influenced Edgar Allan Poe. Her beaten body was found in the Hudson River, and the mysterious circumstances surrounding her death inspired Poe to craft the detective story "The Mystery of Marie Roget." The unsolved nature of Mary Rogers' murder and the subsequent lack of evidence and suspects added a layer of intrigue that Poe masterfully wove into his literary work.

227. ANSWER: B. CONTAMINATION OF EVIDENCE BY ONLOOKERS

The Hall-Mills murders, involving Pastor Edward Hall and Eleanor Mills in New Brunswick, New Jersey, were particularly brutal and remain unsolved due to significant evidence contamination. Witnesses frequently altered their statements, and critical evidence was destroyed or tampered with by onlookers at the crime scene. Additionally, the intense media scrutiny and false confessions further complicated the investigation, preventing the police from identifying the true perpetrators.

228. ANSWER: C. IT INVOLVED A SUSPECTED SEX OFFENDER BUT NO ARRESTS WERE MADE

Betty Shanks was brutally murdered in 1952 in Brisbane, Australia. Despite suspicions pointing towards a known sex offender, no arrests were made. The case is particularly notable for the numerous false confessions that emerged, driven by attention seekers, which further muddied the investigation. The lack of concrete evidence and the persistence of these false leads ensured that Betty Shanks' killer remains unidentified, highlighting the challenges faced by law enforcement in the pre-forensic era.

229. ANSWER: C. ONLOOKERS OFTEN TRAMPLED AND TOOK SOUVENIRS FROM CRIME SCENES

Prior to the advent of forensic science, particularly before 1910, crime scene management was virtually non-existent. When a body was found, police often took time to arrive, allowing neighbors and onlookers to walk through the area freely. This lack of control led to evidence being trampled, disturbed, or even taken as souvenirs by curious bystanders. Such practices severely hampered investigations, resulting in numerous unsolved cases due to the destruction and loss of critical evidence.

230. ANSWER: A. SHE ACTIVELY PARTICIPATED IN THE RAPES

Rosemary West was not just an accomplice but an active participant in the horrific crimes committed alongside her husband, Fred West. Together, they raped, tortured, and murdered twelve girls and young women in their Gloucester home. Rosemary's involvement was direct and brutal, as she watched and participated in the sexual assaults, making her complicit in the unimaginable atrocities they committed. Their partnership in crime was fueled by their shared twisted backgrounds, making them one of the most depraved serial killer couples in history.

231. ANSWER: C. ALL THEIR POSSESSIONS, INCLUDING CARS, WERE LEFT UNTOUCHED

On June 7, 1992, Sherill Levitt, her daughter Suzanne Streeter, and Stacy McCall vanished from Levitt's home in Springfield. The absence of any signs of struggle or forced entry made the disappearance even more chilling. All their belongings, including purses and cars, remained intact, deepening the mystery. Despite extensive investigations and two suspects, Dustin Recla and Robert Cox, no arrests have been made, leaving the fate of the Springfield Three an enduring enigma that continues to terrify and baffle true crime enthusiasts.

232. ANSWER: C. 2001

Jodi Huisentruit, a beloved news anchor, mysteriously disappeared in June 1995 after informing a coworker she was running late. Despite being seen near her red Mazda and reports of a possible struggle, she never returned home. In May 2001, after six years of uncertainty and a lack of evidence, Jodi was legally declared dead. The absence of her body and the unresolved nature of her disappearance continue to haunt her family and the community, making it one of the most perplexing unsolved cases in true crime history.

233. ANSWER: B. CANDY WRAPPERS AND A PENCIL

Nine-year-old Asha Degree vanished in February 2000 from her North Carolina home, leaving her family in despair. Witnesses reported seeing her walking alone early in the morning with her backpack. A crucial clue emerged when items believed to be from her backpack, including candy wrappers, a pencil, a green marker, and a yellow hairbow, were found near the highway. Despite these findings, the absence of her body and the unclear circumstances of her disappearance leave investigators and her family without answers, fueling ongoing speculation about abduction versus voluntary disappearance.

234. ANSWER: C. HIS JOURNALS DEPICTED VIOLENCE TOWARDS WOMEN

Amy Wroe Betchel disappeared in 1997 after running errands and going for a run in Wyoming. Initial theories ranged from animal attacks to voluntary disappearance until detectives uncovered disturbing journals belonging to her husband, Steve Betchel. These journals contained violent imagery and references to harming women, casting a shadow of suspicion over him. Despite lack of concrete evidence linking him to Amy's disappearance, Steve's refusal to cooperate and his suspicious behavior kept him under scrutiny. The involvement of Dale Wayne Eaton, a convicted murderer, further complicates the case, leaving Amy's fate unresolved and shrouded in mystery.

235. ANSWER: B. ONLY FOUR OUT OF TEN CHILDREN WERE ACCOUNTED FOR

On Christmas Eve 1945, the Sodder family house in West Virginia was engulfed in flames. While some family members escaped, five of the ten children were never found. The absence of remains and the suspicious circumstances surrounding the fire—such as the missing ladder and conflicting witness accounts—have fueled endless theories of abduction and foul play. Alleged discoveries of human remains were later debunked, leaving the Sodder children's disappearance an enduring and haunting mystery that continues to puzzle investigators and true crime aficionados alike.

236. ANSWER: C. VIOLENT IMAGERY IN HIS JOURNALS

Amy Wroe Betchel vanished in 1997 after a day of running errands in Wyoming. Investigations revealed that her husband, Steve Betchel, possessed journals containing violent depictions and references to harming women. This disturbing evidence suggested a possible motive, raising suspicions about his involvement in Amy's disappearance. Despite his denial and lack of direct evidence, Steve's troubling writings kept him under police suspicion, highlighting the complex interplay of personal trauma and potential criminal behavior in unsolved true crime cases.

237. ANSWER: B. THE WOMAN IN THE PICTURE RESEMBLED TARA AND HAD A MATCHING SCAR

Tara Calico disappeared while riding her bike in Belen, New Mexico, in 1988. Years later, in 1989, a Polaroid photo was discovered depicting a woman and a young boy bound and gagged, with the woman bearing a scar identical to Tara's. Although some believe the photo shows Tara, others dispute the connection. This eerie resemblance reignited interest in her case, but without definitive evidence, Tara's fate remains unknown. The photo serves as a haunting symbol of unresolved disappearances and the lingering hope for answers.

238. ANSWER: C. HE WAS NEVER BOBBY DUNBAR

Bobby Dunbar vanished at the age of four in 1912, leading to a nationwide search. A boy named Bruce was found and believed to be Bobby, but decades later, in 2004, DNA testing revealed he was not the missing Bobby Dunbar. The true fate of the original Bobby remains a mystery, leaving unanswered questions about whether he was kidnapped, perished in an accident, or met some other unknown end. This case highlights the complexities and enduring uncertainties in missing person investigations.

239. ANSWER: C. SHE ESCAPED AND ALERTED AUTHORITIES

Kate Moir was the only survivor of Catherine and David Birnie's brutal murder spree. After being kidnapped, chained, and raped by David, Kate was forced to call her parents to prevent suspicion. However, when Catherine answered the doorbell, Kate seized the moment to escape by jumping out the window and running to a grocery store. There, she successfully contacted the police, providing critical information that led to the Birnies' arrest. Kate's brave escape was pivotal in bringing the killers to justice, ending their horrific reign and preventing further murders.

240. ANSWER: C. ELIMINATING UNWANTED INDIVIDUALS

Ray and Faye Copeland targeted and murdered drifters whom they had hired for work. Their motive centered around eliminating individuals they deemed unnecessary once the victims were no longer useful. By luring these men into their van under the guise of employment, Ray systematically killed them to dispose of the bodies discreetly. Faye's involvement remains uncertain, but her role in maintaining the facade of normalcy allowed Ray to carry out his gruesome acts without immediate detection. Their chilling method of selecting and disposing of victims underscores the calculated and predatory nature of their crimes.

241. ANSWER: B. VILLISCA, IOWA

The Ax Murder House is infamously located in Villisca, Iowa. In 1912, Catherine and David Birnie brutally murdered the Moore family and two sisters from a local family in their home. The heinous crime involved murdering all seven victims with an ax while they were asleep. The killer remained in the house for hours, committing atrocities without being detected until the morning. Despite numerous investigations, the Ax Murder House remains a chilling unsolved case, haunting the community with its gruesome legacy.

242. ANSWER: C. THE FAMILY WAS UNAWARE OF THE INTRUDER UNTIL IT WAS TOO LATE

The Ax Murder House case is particularly terrifying because Catherine and David Birnie were able to murder the Moore family and two sisters without the victims realizing an intruder was present until it was too late. The family was peacefully returning from church activities when they were brutally attacked while asleep. The intruder remained in the house for hours, making the situation even more horrifying as the family had no idea they were being targeted until the morning when their bodies were discovered.

243. ANSWER: C. SHE CALLED THE POLICE FROM A GROCERY STORE

Kate Moir was the only survivor of Catherine and David Birnie's brutal murder spree. After being kidnapped, chained, and raped by David while Catherine watched, Kate was forced to call her parents to avoid raising suspicion. Catherine briefly unchained her to use the phone, but when the doorbell rang, Catherine stepped away to answer it. Seizing this opportunity, Kate jumped out of the window and fled to the nearest grocery store, where she successfully contacted the police. Her courageous escape led to the Birnies' arrest, ending their reign of terror and saving countless potential victims.

244. ANSWER: D. PROMISING JOB OPPORTUNITIES

Catherine and David Birnie lured their victims by offering them rides or job opportunities. They targeted unsuspecting women and young men, gaining their trust by appearing friendly and offering assistance. Once inside the car, the Birnies would brutally attack and murder their victims, using their deceitful tactics to carry out their heinous crimes without immediate suspicion.

245. ANSWER: C. HE STRUCK HER IN THE HEAD WITH AN AX

After Denise Brown, one of the Birnies' victims, sat up in her shallow grave, David Birnie panicked and grabbed an ax to ensure her death. He struck her in the head twice, making certain that she would not survive. This gruesome act solidified the Birnies' brutal modus operandi, involving luring victims into their home, chaining them to the bed, raping them, and ultimately murdering them with an ax.

246. ANSWER: C. HE BEAT HER UNTIL SHE REFUSED TO CRY

Fred West subjected his stepdaughter Charmaine to relentless physical abuse, brutally beating her until she stopped crying. This extreme violence was part of a larger pattern of torture and murder carried out by Fred and his wife, Rosemary West. Their sadistic acts included rape and the eventual disappearance of Charmaine, marking them as one of the most heinous serial killer couples in history. Their crimes left a lasting scar on Gloucester, revealing the depths of their depravity.

247. ANSWER: C. DISCOVERY OF BODIES IN THEIR GARDEN

Ian Brady and Myra Hindley were ultimately captured when police obtained a search warrant for their home and discovered the remains of several victims buried in their garden. This gruesome find provided the necessary evidence to convict the couple of their heinous crimes. The unearthing of the bodies along Saddleworth Moor exposed the full extent of their murderous spree, ending their reign of terror and ensuring they would never harm another victim.

248. ANSWER: C. THE STACKING OF BODIES IN THE BARN

The Gruber family murders in Bavaria, Germany, were particularly horrifying due to the method of disposing of the victims' bodies. After brutally killing five family members and their maid, the killer stacked the bodies in the barn, making the scene even more gruesome and unsettling. This method of body disposal highlighted the sheer brutality and lack of remorse exhibited by the murderer, leaving the community in fear and the case unsolved to this day.

249. ANSWER: B. THERE WAS NO SIGN OF FORCED ENTRY

The Robison family's bodies were discovered in Lake Michigan twenty-seven days after their disappearance, with no signs of forced entry at their cottage. The absence of struggle or signs of a break-in made the case particularly mysterious and chilling. The family's truck was found abandoned with their belongings, and despite finding gunshot residue on their son Eddie's hands, no one was ever convicted of the murders. The case remains one of the most haunting unsolved mysteries, leaving investigators and true crime enthusiasts alike to ponder the dark forces that led to the family's tragic end.

250. ANSWER: C. THE TWO YOUNGER BROTHERS AND ONE FRIEND WERE UNHARMED

The Keddie Cabin Murders in 1981 are particularly strange because while Sheila Sharp, her mother, brother, and a family friend were brutally murdered in cabin 28 at the Keddie Resort Lodge, the two younger brothers and one of their friends were found unharmed in another bedroom. Additionally, the twelve-year-old Tina was missing and was later found dead fifty miles away, adding to the baffling nature of the case. Despite thorough investigations and identifying two main suspects, Marty Smartt and Bo Boubede, the case remains unsolved, continuing to haunt true crime enthusiasts with its perplexing details.

251. ANSWER: B. SHE RECORDED HER ABUSE AND SHOWED IT TO FRIENDS

Charmaine, Fred West's stepdaughter, played a pivotal role in uncovering the Wests' crimes by recording herself being raped and abused by Fred. These recordings were shown to her friends at school, who then alerted her mother. This crucial evidence prompted a police investigation that eventually led to the discovery of multiple victims' remains in the Wests' home. Charmaine's brave actions were instrumental in bringing the heinous crimes of Fred and Rosemary West to light, ending their reign of terror.

252. ANSWER: B. THE YOUNGER SIBLINGS WERE UNHARMED

The Keddie Cabin Murders are especially mysterious because while several family members and a friend were brutally killed, the two younger brothers and one friend were found unharmed in another bedroom. Additionally, the twelve-year-old Tina was missing and was later found dead fifty miles away. This selective violence and the survival of some members added layers of complexity to the case, making it one of the most perplexing unsolved mysteries in true crime history.

253. ANSWER: B. JOSEPH SCOLARO III

Joseph Scolaro III was the primary suspect in the Robison family murders in Lake Michigan. Although he had embezzled money from Mr. Robison and was connected to the crime, he was never tried for the murders. Scolaro committed suicide, leaving behind a note expressing regret but maintaining his innocence. This prevented any further legal action, leaving the case unsolved and adding to its enduring mystery.

254. ANSWER: B. THE PRESENCE OF THE KILLER IN THE HOME FOR HOURS

The Ax Murder House case is particularly grotesque because Catherine and David Birnie remained inside the Moore family's home for several hours after committing the murders. During this time, the killer not only brutally killed the victims but also lingered in the house, committing further atrocities and leaving behind evidence of their presence. This prolonged stay in the crime scene heightened the horror, as the family had no idea they were being targeted until the morning discovery.

255. ANSWER: C. THE KILLER'S IDENTITY REMAINS UNKNOWN

The Walker family murders remain an unsolved mystery since 1959, with no definitive answers about who killed them. The family, consisting of Mr. Clifford Walker, Mrs. Christine Walker, and their two children, were found brutally murdered in their home. Despite several suspects, including Emmett Monroe Spencer who confessed but was deemed unreliable, the true perpetrator was never identified. This unresolved case continues to perplex investigators and true crime enthusiasts alike.

256. ANSWER: C. DNA SAMPLES

The Ax Murder House case occurred in 1912, long before the advent of DNA testing and with fingerprinting just emerging as a forensic tool. This lack of advanced forensic technology meant that crucial evidence was either nonexistent or easily destroyed by the influx of curious townspeople who visited the crime scene. As a result, the police were unable to collect sufficient evidence to identify and capture the killer, leaving the case unsolved and shrouded in mystery.

257. ANSWER: C. THEY CHAINED VICTIMS TO BEDS AND ACTED LIKE FAMILY

Catherine and David Birnie used the chilling strategy of luring victims into their home under false pretenses, such as offering rides or job opportunities. Once inside, they chained the victims to the bed, allowing David to rape them repeatedly while Catherine watched. This horrifying method of captivity and abuse masked their true intentions, making the murders appear as violent intrusions rather than premeditated acts of serial killing. Their deceptive tactics helped them maintain a facade of normalcy while committing their gruesome crimes.

258. ANSWER: A. THE LACK OF MODERN FORENSIC METHODS

The Ade family murders in 1847 were particularly challenging to solve due to the absence of modern forensic techniques such as DNA testing and comprehensive fingerprinting. Additionally, the case involved gruesome acts like decapitation and partial skull removal, but the lack of advanced investigative tools at the time meant that no one was ever convicted for these crimes. The house was eventually torn down, and the murders remain one of the most haunting unsolved cases in history.

259. ANSWER: C. BOTH CASES INVOLVED INTRUDERS STAYING INSIDE THE HOUSE

Both the Keddie Cabin Murders and the Ax Murder House case involved intruders who stayed inside the victims' homes for extended periods. In the Ax Murder House case, Catherine and David Birnie remained inside for hours after committing the murders, while in the Keddie Cabin Murders, the killer(s) stayed at the lodge after killing the victims. This similarity added to the horror and mystery of both cases, as the presence of the intruder within the home intensified the fear and complexity of solving these brutal crimes.

260. ANSWER: B. BECAUSE THE CRIMES TOOK PLACE IN A MOORLAND AREA

The Moors Murders, committed by Ian Brady and Myra Hindley between 1963 and 1965, derived their name from the Saddleworth Moor area where many of the victims were buried. This moorland setting added a haunting and desolate backdrop to the gruesome crimes, enhancing the eerie and unsettling nature of the case. The name has since become synonymous with one of the most notorious serial killer cases in British history.

261. ANSWER: B. A ROBBERY GONE WRONG

Jacob Ade, a wealthy farmer, was believed to have murdered his family in a fit of greed driven by their wealth. The police initially thought the horrific murders, which included decapitations and other mutilations, were motivated by robbery. However, the discovery of burnt remnants of money at the crime scene only added to the sinister nature of the crime, making it one of the most gruesome unsolved cases in history.

262. ANSWER: C. THEY COMMITTED SUICIDE

Ray and Faye Copeland, the oldest couple ever sentenced to death in the United States, both died before their death sentences could be carried out. Ray died of natural causes while awaiting execution, and Faye suffered a stroke and was released to a nursing home, where she passed away in 2003. Their deaths prevented any further legal proceedings and left the case officially unsolved.

263. ANSWER: C. SHE PROVIDED LOGISTICAL SUPPORT AND INFORMATION

Faye Copeland was sentenced to sixteen years in prison after agreeing to testify against her husband, Ray Copeland. While her exact involvement in the murders remains unclear, evidence such as the list of victims' names written in her handwriting suggested her complicity. Her cooperation with the authorities led to a lighter sentence compared to Ray, who was sentenced to death. This decision highlighted the complexity of her role in the crimes and the limited consequences she faced despite the severity of their actions.

264. ANSWER: B. DESIRE FOR WEALTH

The primary motive behind the Ade family murders was believed to be greed. Jacob Ade, a wealthy farmer, was suspected of killing his family to seize their substantial wealth. The discovery of burned remnants of money in the rubble supported the theory that the murders were financially motivated. This horrific act of violence underscores the lengths to which some individuals will go driven by avarice, leaving a lasting legacy of fear and mystery surrounding the case.

265. ANSWER: C. IT ALERTED THE AUTHORITIES ABOUT KATE MOIR'S LOCATION

The phone call made by Kate Moir was pivotal in ending Catherine and David Birnie's murder spree. After being forced to call her parents to avoid raising suspicion, Kate took advantage of Catherine's brief absence to escape through a window. Upon reaching the nearest grocery store, Kate successfully contacted the police and provided them with the Birnies' address. This crucial call led to the swift arrest of Catherine and David Birnie, effectively stopping their horrific killing spree and bringing justice for their victims.

266. ANSWER: B. DECAPITATION AND SKULL REMOVAL

The Ade family faced an exceptionally gruesome murder method in 1847, involving decapitation and the removal of parts of their skulls. Jacob Ade brutally killed his family and then set their home on fire, leaving behind horrifying evidence of the murders. The mutilation of the victims' bodies added a macabre layer to the crime, making it one of the most disturbing and unsolved cases in true crime history.

267. ANSWER: B. ALONG A SNOWY ROAD

On December 28, 1956, twelve-year-old Patricia and fifteen-year-old Barbara Grimes went to watch "Love Me Tender" at the movies but never returned home. Their naked bodies were discovered on January 22, 1957, along a deserted road. The autopsy reports were baffling, with three forensic pathologists unable to agree on the exact cause and time of death. Despite numerous sightings of the sisters weeks after their disappearance, the case remains one of Australia's most mysterious unsolved murders.

268. ANSWER: B. MULTIPLE CONFLICTING AUTOPSY REPORTS

The Grimes sisters' murders are shrouded in mystery due to conflicting autopsy reports. While the autopsies suggested the girls were killed within five hours of being taken, witnesses reported seeing them weeks later. Additionally, puncture wounds on their bodies were attributed to rodent activity by pathologists, making it unclear how and when the sisters actually died. This inconsistency has left investigators and the public puzzled for decades.

269. ANSWER: B. A MAN RESEMBLING ELVIS PRESLEY

The last known sighting of Patricia and Barbara Grimes was when they were seen talking to a young man who resembled Elvis Presley. Witnesses reported that the sisters got into his Mercury car after their conversation. This mysterious encounter with a man dressed similarly to the iconic singer added an eerie twist to the case, leaving authorities with more questions than answers about the true identity of their killer.

270. ANSWER: C. SHOCK AND EXPOSURE

Despite the presence of puncture wounds on Patricia and Barbara Grimes, the autopsists concluded that the girls died from shock and exposure. The cold weather likely slowed decomposition, complicating the determination of the exact time and cause of death. This conclusion contradicted some witness reports and added to the perplexity surrounding the sisters' tragic demise.

271. ANSWER: D. CONFLICTING AUTOPSY RESULTS

The Grimes sisters' case remains unsolved primarily due to conflicting autopsy results that obscured the true cause and timing of their deaths. While some pathologists believed the girls were killed within hours of their disappearance, eyewitness accounts suggested they might have been alive weeks later. This discrepancy made it difficult for investigators to piece together the events leading to the murders, leaving the case open and the perpetrators unidentified.

272. ANSWER: B. REMOVING HIS PENIS AFTER BEING SHOT

Russell Keith Dardeen's gruesome end was marked by a horrifying mutilation—after being shot, his penis was removed. Found in a wheat field a few miles from his trailer, Russell's body bore the scars of this savage attack. His murder of Elaine and their newborn baby, along with his own brutal demise, remains one of the most disturbing cases in Australian true crime history.

273. ANSWER: A. THE FAMILY HAD NO ENEMIES

The Dardeen family's murder was particularly shocking because they seemed like a happy and unassuming family with no known enemies. On November 18, 1987, Elaine and her son Peter were found brutally beaten to death along with their newborn baby. The absence of any motive or known adversaries made the case even more perplexing, deepening the mystery surrounding the killings.

274. ANSWER: C. TOMMY LYNN SELLS

Tommy Lynn Sells was a prime suspect in the brutal murders of Elaine and Peter Dardeen, as well as their newborn baby. Although he confessed to the murders, his confessions were inconsistent and later recanted. Sells was executed for another crime before he could be officially charged with the Dardeen murders, leaving the case unresolved and the true perpetrator unknown.

275. ANSWER: B. EVISCERATING A VICTIM WITH MASONIC SYMBOLS

Clive, obsessed with accurately recreating the crimes of infamous serial killers, planned to eviscerate a victim while integrating Masonic symbols if Jack the Ripper was selected on the Thrill-Kill wheel. This disturbing plan highlighted his twisted fascination with the ritualistic and symbolic aspects of murder, aiming to emulate the legendary brutality and mysterious aura surrounding Jack the Ripper.

276. ANSWER: C. DISCOVERY OF BODIES BURIED IN THEIR GARDEN

Ian Brady and Myra Hindley were finally arrested when police obtained a search warrant for their home and uncovered the remains of several victims buried in their garden. This grisly discovery provided the concrete evidence needed to convict the couple of their heinous crimes. The uncovering of these bodies along Saddleworth Moor marked the end of one of the most notorious serial killing sprees in British history, ensuring that Ian and Myra would never harm another victim.

277. ANSWER: B. THE LIGHTHOUSE LIGHT BEING EXTINGUISHED

On December 15, 1900, a steamship passing by the Flannan Isles noticed that the lighthouse light was not operational. This unusual observation led to reports being made, sparking an investigation into the disappearance of the three lighthouse keepers. The absence of the light, combined with subsequent findings of unlit fires and stopped clocks, deepened the mystery surrounding the unexplained vanishing of the lighthouse residents.

278. ANSWER: C. FIRES HAD NOT BEEN LIT IN DAYS AND CLOCKS HAD STOPPED

When Joseph Moore went ashore to investigate the Flannan Isles lighthouse, he discovered eerie signs indicating something was terribly wrong. The kitchen door was open, but all beds were empty, fires had not been lit for days, and the clocks had stopped. These unsettling findings suggested that the lighthouse keepers had vanished without a trace, leaving behind a scene of abrupt abandonment and raising more questions about their disappearance.

279. ANSWER: B. THE WORD "CROATOAN"

Upon returning to the Roanoke Colony three years after its establishment in 1587, Governor John White found the settlement completely deserted with no signs of struggle. The only clue left behind was the word "Croatoan" carved into a tree, which was the name of an indigenous tribe allied with the colonists. This enigmatic message has fueled decades of speculation and theories regarding the fate of the lost colonists, with no definitive answers remaining to this day.

280. ANSWER: C. HER BODY WAS BURNED WITH PARTS STILL INTACT, AND NO SIGNS OF A HIGH-TEMPERATURE FIRE

Mary Reeser's death in 1951 remains one of the most baffling mysteries due to the inexplicable condition in which she was found. Her body was almost entirely ash except for her left foot in a satin slipper, and her skull had shrunk from the heat. Strangely, her upholstered chair was destroyed, yet there were no scorch marks in the apartment, and items like light switches and candlesticks showed signs of melting without a corresponding intense fire. This inconsistency has left investigators and the public questioning whether it was spontaneous combustion or foul play.

281. ANSWER: C. SHE SAW A SPECIFIC INDIVIDUAL FIRING THE GUN

During the murder of Ken McElroy in Skidmore, Missouri, his wife was the only person who claimed to have seen the shooter. Despite her testimony, no one else in the crowd came forward to identify the shooter, leading to no arrests or charges being filed. This collective silence from the crowd ensured that the perpetrator remained anonymous, highlighting the town's unanimous desire to rid themselves of McElroy without facing legal repercussions.

282. ANSWER: D. SHE INTERACTED WITH HIM MULTIPLE TIMES DURING HIS STAY

The maid at the Hotel President in Kansas City played a crucial role in the mysterious death of Roland T. Owen (later revealed as Artemus Ogletree). She interacted with him multiple times, including cleaning his room and responding to his requests not to lock the door. Her observations of his strange behavior, such as staying in the dark and drawing blinds, and her eventual discovery of his gruesome condition after he was found tied and stabbed, were pivotal in piecing together the disturbing events that led to his untimely death.

283. ANSWER: B. THE ROOM WAS FOUND LOCKED FROM THE OUTSIDE

The death of Roland T. Owen, whose true identity was later revealed as Artemus Ogletree, remains shrouded in mystery due to the peculiar circumstances of his demise. The hotel room was locked from the outside, yet Owen was found tied up, stabbed, and left with a bloodstain on his bedding. Despite several attempts to communicate and repeated knocks, no one could access the room, leading to unanswered questions about how he was attacked and by whom, making the case an enduring unsolved mystery.

284. ANSWER: C. LIGHT SWITCHES AND CANDLESTICKS HAD MELTED BUT OTHER ITEMS REMAINED UNDAMAGED

In Mary Reeser's apartment, despite her body being severely burned, several inconsistencies suggested that a high-temperature fire was unlikely. While light switches and candlesticks had melted, indicating some exposure to heat, other items like outlets remained functional, and newspapers nearby were undamaged despite being combustible. Additionally, the chair she was sitting on was destroyed, yet there were no scorch marks elsewhere in the apartment. These contradictory signs have fueled ongoing debates about whether her death was due to spontaneous combustion or another mysterious cause.

285. ANSWER: C. THEIR DISAPPEARANCE REMAINS UNEXPLAINED

Despite thorough investigations following the disappearance of the three lighthouse keepers at Flannan Isles in 1900, no definitive explanation has been found. The eerie signs of abandonment and the lack of evidence have left the case unresolved for over a century, continuing to intrigue and terrify those interested in unsolved mysteries and maritime lore.

286. ANSWER: A. A CARVED CROSS

Before leaving the Roanoke Colony in 1587 to seek supplies, Governor John White instructed the colonists to carve a cross into a tree if they were forced to abandon the settlement. Upon his return three years later, he discovered that the colony had vanished without a trace, and no crosses were found. The absence of this marker added to the enigma surrounding the disappearance of the Roanoke colonists, leaving historians and enthusiasts to ponder the fate of the lost settlers.

287. ANSWER: B. THEY BELIEVED IT WAS THE ONLY WAY TO RID THE TOWN OF HIS TYRANNY

The residents of Skidmore, Missouri, took justice into their own hands by murdering Ken McElroy, a violent bully who terrorized the town. Frustrated by the authorities' inability to prosecute him, the townspeople felt that killing him was the only solution to end his reign of terror. This collective action, carried out by an anonymous mob during a town meeting, resulted in McElroy's death without any subsequent arrests or charges, reflecting the extreme measures the community felt compelled to take to restore peace.

288. ANSWER: C. OWEN WAS ON THE BED NAKED WITH A DARK STAIN ON THE BEDDING

When the maid returned to clean Room 1046 at the Hotel President after Roland T. Owen had been staying there, she found him lying naked on the bed with a dark stain surrounding him. This horrifying discovery, combined with other signs of foul play such as cords tying him up and stab wounds, heightened the mystery surrounding his death. Despite his plea that "Nobody" had hurt him, the circumstances of his demise remained inexplicable, leading to further intrigue and unresolved questions.

289. ANSWER: C. OWEN WAS STILL IN THE ROOM, SITTING IN THE DARK

Upon returning to Room 1046 the morning after Roland T. Owen's initial visit, the maid found him still present, sitting in the darkness despite the room being locked from the outside. Owen responded to the phone, claiming he had just eaten and wasn't hungry, adding another layer of mystery to the situation. His continued presence despite the locked door and his odd behavior deepened the perplexing nature of his eventual tragic end.

290. ANSWER: C. CROATOAN

Upon returning to the deserted Roanoke Colony, Governor John White found the word "Croatoan" carved into a tree, offering the only clue about the colonists' disappearance. This term was the name of an indigenous tribe allied with the settlers, suggesting possible relocation or assimilation. However, no further evidence was found to confirm the fate of the colonists, leaving the mystery of the lost Roanoke Colony unsolved for centuries.

291. ANSWER: C. HER BODY WAS BURNED WHILE OTHER ITEMS REMAINED MOSTLY UNDAMAGED

The mysterious death of Mary Reeser raised suspicions due to the fact that while her body was extensively burned, other items in her apartment showed minimal signs of a high-temperature fire. The chair she was sitting on was destroyed, but there were no scorch marks, and items like newspapers remained intact. Additionally, light switches and candlesticks had melted inconsistently, leading investigators to question whether her death was due to spontaneous combustion or foul play, as the evidence did not align with a typical fire scenario.

292. ANSWER: B. THERE WERE NO SIGNS OF FORCED ENTRY OR STRUGGLE

The disappearance of the Flannan Isles lighthouse keepers remains one of the most perplexing maritime mysteries due to the absence of any signs of forced entry or struggle. When Joseph Moore investigated, he found the lighthouse seemingly undisturbed with closed gates and unlit fires, but no evidence pointed to violence or abduction. This lack of concrete clues has left the fate of the keepers shrouded in mystery for over a century.

293. ANSWER: B. MULTIPLE VOICES WERE HEARD INSIDE

The maid encountered a chilling phenomenon when she heard loud voices coming from inside Room 1046 at the Hotel President after Roland T. Owen had been staying there. Despite knocking and attempting to clean the room, the voices insisted they didn't need any more towels. This eerie occurrence, coupled with Owen's subsequent violent death, intensified the mystery surrounding the events in Room 1046, leaving questions about the nature of the voices and the true circumstances of his murder.

294. ANSWER: C. THEY ASSIMILATED WITH THE CROATOAN TRIBE

The primary theory regarding the disappearance of the Roanoke Colony is that the colonists assimilated with the Croatoan tribe, an indigenous group allied with the settlers. Governor John White found the word "Croatoan" carved on a tree, suggesting a possible relocation or integration with the local population. However, no definitive evidence has been found to confirm this theory, leaving the true fate of the Roanoke colonists a lasting historical mystery.

295. ANSWER: D. DISCOVERY OF MULTIPLE HUMAN REMAINS AT THEIR HOME

Fred and Rosemary West were convicted for their serial murders after the discovery of multiple human remains buried at their Gloucester home. The excavation of their property revealed the bodies of several victims, including Anne McFall, Charmaine, and Catherine Costello. This overwhelming physical evidence provided the necessary proof to convict the couple, ending their spree of rape, torture, and murder that had terrorized the community.

296. ANSWER: D. ALL OF THE ABOVE

All three of these notorious killers met their end in prison, not by the hands of the justice system, but by other inmates. Jeffrey Dahmer was bludgeoned to death by fellow inmate Christopher Scarver in 1994, supposedly because Dahmer was taunting inmates by shaping his food to look like body parts. Daniel Camargo Barbosa was stabbed in prison in the same year by the nephew of one of his victims, while Albert DeSalvo, the infamous Boston Strangler, was also stabbed to death in 1973.

297. ANSWER: C. LAWRENCE BITTAKER AND ROY NORRIS

Lawrence Bittaker and Roy Norris, known as the Toolbox Killers, are considered among the most depraved killers in U.S. history. After meeting in prison, they teamed up to abduct, torture, and murder teenage girls in California. Their tools of choice—pliers, screwdrivers, and ice picks—gave them their infamous nickname. The pair even recorded their crimes, and the resulting tapes were so horrifying that many of those involved in their trial were left in tears.

298. ANSWER: TRUE

To help actors Jodie Foster and Scott Glenn prepare for *The Silence of the Lambs*, renowned FBI profiler John Douglas played tapes recorded by the Toolbox Killers for Glenn. The tapes documented the torture and murders committed by Lawrence Bittaker and Roy Norris, giving Glenn a chilling understanding of the psychological depth of real-life killers, which he used to shape his portrayal of FBI agent Jack Crawford.

299. ANSWER: D. BOTH A AND C

The investigation into Russian serial killer Andrei Chikatilo, known as the Butcher of Rostov, was riddled with errors. In 1983, Aleksandr Kravchenko was wrongfully executed for Chikatilo's first murder, and another man arrested in connection with the crimes later committed suicide while in custody. Chikatilo was eventually convicted of 52 murders in 1992 and was executed in 1994.

300. ANSWER: B. HANGED WITH THE SAME CHAIN HE USED ON HIS VICTIMS

Javed Iqbal confessed to killing 100 boys in Lahore, Pakistan, in the late 1990s. After luring the boys to his home, he would strangle them with a chain and dissolve their bodies in acid. Though he later recanted his confession, he was sentenced to death by hanging with the very same chain he used on his victims. Before the sentence could be carried out, Iqbal was found dead in his cell, with his death ruled a suicide under suspicious circumstances.

301. ANSWER: A. SANTA CLAUS

Bruce McArthur, a landscaper and serial killer, also worked as a shopping mall Santa Claus during the holiday season. McArthur was responsible for the murders of eight men between 2010 and 2017, most of whom were from Toronto's Gay Village. Despite several red flags over the years, including a strangulation attempt in 2016, McArthur's crimes went undetected for nearly a decade.

302. ANSWER: TRUE

Lao Rongzhi, along with her boyfriend Fa Ziying, was responsible for the murders of seven people in the 1990s. After Fa was executed for the crimes in 1999, Rongzhi evaded capture for two decades by living under various false identities. She was finally apprehended in 2019 and sentenced to death in 2021. Rongzhi claims she was coerced by her abusive partner, but the court found her equally culpable.

303. ANSWER: B. SHOOT ALCALA IN COURT

Marianne Connelly, the mother of Rodney Alcala's victim Robin Samsoe, carried a loaded handgun with the intention of shooting Alcala during his 1980 trial. She later abandoned her plan, realizing she needed to be there for her other children. Despite this, Alcala's first two convictions were overturned on appeal, and it wasn't until 2010 that he was convicted for the third time. Alcala died in prison in 2021.

304. ANSWER: A. JOHN COOPER

Welsh serial killer John Cooper appeared on a quiz show called *Bullseye* in 1989, just weeks before he murdered a couple, Peter and Gwenda Dixon. Cooper had already killed siblings Helen and Richard Thomas in 1985, and the cases went cold until forensic evidence linked him to the unsolved murders. Footage from his appearance on *Bullseye* was used in his trial to help convict him of the crimes.

305. ANSWER: A. JOHN WAYNE GACY

In 1978, John Wayne Gacy, known as the Killer Clown for his horrifying murders of over 30 young men, was photographed shaking hands with First Lady Rosalynn Carter. At the time, Gacy had received security clearance to meet her, and a White House photographer captured the moment. The photo later made headlines after Gacy's arrest, with Carter's autograph on the image reading: "To John Gacy, best wishes."

306. ANSWER: D. BOTH B AND C

Both Ted Bundy and Arthur Shawcross, despite their horrific crimes, have moments where they saved lives. Ted Bundy once rescued a young girl from drowning in Seattle's Green Lake in 1970. Arthur Shawcross, while serving time for robbery and arson, helped save a correctional officer during a prison riot, which led to his early release. However, both went on to commit numerous murders after these incidents.

307. ANSWER: B. HE NEVER PHYSICALLY KILLED ANYONE HIMSELF

Charles Manson stands out in the annals of serial killers as he orchestrated a series of brutal and unprovoked murders without personally committing any of them.

Instead, he manipulated and controlled his followers, known as "The Family," to carry out his heinous plans. Manson's ability to influence and direct his cult members to murder high-profile victims, including actress Sharon Tate, showcases his mastery of manipulation and control, making his story both chilling and bizarre.

308. ANSWER: B. SPAHN'S MOVIE RANCH, AN ABANDONED FILM SET

Before embarking on their murderous spree, Charles Manson and his followers settled at Spahn's Movie Ranch, an abandoned film set near Los Angeles. This secluded location provided the perfect hideout for "The Family," allowing them to live in isolation while Manson exerted his control over the group. The ranch became the base from which Manson directed his followers to commit the infamous Tate-LaBianca murders, further cementing his legacy as a manipulative cult leader.

309. ANSWER: C. SIMILAR WRITINGS LEFT AT BOTH CRIME SCENES

The initial connection between the Tate and LaBianca murders and Charles Manson was established through the similar writings left at both crime scenes. Phrases like "Pig" and "War" were daubed in the victims' blood, indicating a common motive and method. These symbolic messages aligned with Manson's delusional belief in an impending race war, known as "Helter Skelter," which he sought to incite through these orchestrated killings.

310. ANSWER: D. HIS TRIAL WAS DECLARED A MISTRIAL

During Charles Manson's first trial, numerous disruptions occurred both inside and outside the courtroom. Manson and his followers frequently interrupted proceedings, and Manson himself attacked Judge Order by leaping from his seat. These chaotic events led to Judge William Keene withdrawing his authority to allow Manson to represent himself, and the trial was eventually declared a mistrial. The court was then presided over by Judge Charles H. Older, who oversaw the remainder of the trial leading to Manson's conviction.

311. ANSWER: C. FORCING EXCESSIVE ALCOHOL CONSUMPTION

Gilbert Paul Jordan, also known as the "Boozing Barber," employed a unique and deceptive method to murder his victims by forcing them to consume excessive amounts of alcohol. Targeting primarily Native American prostitutes in Vancouver's Downtown Eastside, Jordan would lure his victims to his barber shop or a cheap hotel room, encourage them to drink heavily, and then pour more alcohol down their throats until they succumbed to alcohol poisoning. This method allowed him to kill multiple women without raising immediate suspicion.

312. ANSWER: B. MANSLAUGHTER

Gilbert Paul Jordan was initially charged with manslaughter for the murder of Vanessa Lee Buckner, whom he killed by poisoning and raping. Despite the severity of his crime, Jordan was sentenced to fifteen years for manslaughter. His lawyers successfully appealed the sentence, reducing it to nine years, of which Jordan served only six. This lenient sentencing allowed him to continue his killing spree shortly after his release, highlighting significant failures in the justice system.

313. ANSWER: C. HIS FINGERPRINTS WERE FOUND AT THE CRIME SCENES

Gilbert Paul Jordan was finally apprehended when police traced his fingerprints found at multiple crime scenes to his room at a nearby hotel. After receiving an anonymous tip, authorities connected Jordan to the murders of Vanessa Lee Buckner and Edna Shade through forensic evidence. His fingerprints on items left behind at these locations provided the crucial link needed to arrest him, leading to his conviction for multiple murders.

314. ANSWER: B. THE BTK KILLER

Dennis Rader earned the nickname "The BTK Killer," which stands for "Bind, Torture, Kill," describing his method of murdering his victims. Operating between 1974 and 1991, Rader meticulously planned and executed his killings, binding his victims, torturing them, and ultimately killing them. His ability to evade capture for decades, coupled with his calculated approach, made him one of the most notorious and elusive serial killers in American history.

315. ANSWER: C. A FLOPPY DISK HE SENT TO THE POLICE

Dennis Rader was ultimately identified and captured in 2005 after he sent a floppy disk to the police. The disk contained information that allowed investigators to trace it back to Rader's church. Further investigation and a DNA match with evidence from crime scenes confirmed his identity as the BTK Killer. Rader was apprehended near his home in Park City, Kansas, and subsequently pleaded guilty to his crimes, receiving multiple life sentences without the possibility of parole.

316. ANSWER: C. SHOOTING

Aileen Wuornos, unlike most female serial killers who prefer more covert methods like poisoning, used a firearm to kill her victims. She shot her victims at point-blank range with a .22 caliber handgun, targeting men who solicited her for sex. Her choice of a gun as her weapon of choice made her methods more overt and violent compared to her female counterparts, who often employ less direct means.

317. ANSWER: C. SHE ENDURED ABUSE AND A TUMULTUOUS FAMILY LIFE

Aileen Wuornos had a deeply troubled and abusive childhood, which significantly contributed to her descent into serial killing. Born to an adolescent couple, her father was a juvenile pedophile who committed suicide, and her mother abandoned her and her brother. Growing up in an unstable and abusive environment, Aileen faced sexual abuse, neglect, and a lack of parental support. These traumatic experiences fueled her rage and contributed to her later violent behavior.

318. ANSWER: C. HE MAINTAINED A FAÇADE OF NORMALCY AND BLENDED INTO HIS COMMUNITY

Dennis Rader was able to evade capture for decades by maintaining a seemingly normal and unassuming lifestyle. He was an active member of his community, involved in local organizations like the Boy Scouts and his church, and held a steady job with ADT Security. This façade of normalcy allowed him to blend in seamlessly, making it difficult for authorities to suspect him as the BTK Killer. His ability to compartmentalize his life contributed significantly to his prolonged evasion of justice.

319. ANSWER: D. WITNESSES IDENTIFIED HER THROUGH AN ANONYMOUS TIP

Aileen Wuornos' criminal activities in Florida came to light when witnesses identified her through an anonymous tip. After several murders in 1989 and 1990, police received information linking Wuornos and her partner, Tyria Moore, to the crimes based on a bloody palm print left at one of the murder scenes. Although Wuornos and Moore were not together at the time of the murders, the evidence and witness statements eventually led to Wuornos' arrest and subsequent conviction for her crimes.

320. ANSWER: C. THE ROLE OF EARLY CHILDHOOD TRAUMA IN DEVELOPING VIOLENT TENDENCIES

Gilbert Paul Jordan's case provided psychologists with valuable insights into how early childhood trauma and a tumultuous upbringing can contribute to the development of violent tendencies and antisocial behavior. Growing up in a hostile environment, facing abuse, and developing an addiction to alcohol from a young age were significant factors that influenced his descent into a life of crime and eventual transformation into the "Boozing Barber," a serial killer who exploited his victims' vulnerabilities.

321. ANSWER: C. 10 CONSECUTIVE LIFE TERMS

Dennis Rader, known as the BTK Killer, was sentenced to 10 consecutive life terms on August 18, 2005, for his series of murders. Each life term corresponded to one of his victims, ensuring that Rader would spend the remainder of his life in prison without the possibility of parole. This sentencing reflected the severity and premeditated nature of his crimes, bringing a definitive end to his killing spree.

322. ANSWER: C. AS THE ULTIMATE MASTER OF MANIPULATION

Charles Manson saw himself as the ultimate master of manipulation within his cult, "The Family." He exerted complete control over his followers, influencing their actions and directing them to commit murders on his behalf. Manson's ability to manipulate and dominate his cult members showcased his profound psychological influence, enabling him to orchestrate a series of brutal killings without personally participating in the violence.

323. ANSWER: C. RACIALLY CHARGED PHRASES LIKE "PIG" AND "WAR"

Charles Manson wanted to leave racially charged phrases such as "Pig" and "War" at his murder scenes. These messages were part of his delusional plan to incite a race war, which he termed "Helter Skelter," inspired by his interpretation of The Beatles' song. The messages were intended to create the appearance of racially motivated murders by blacks against whites, thereby igniting the conflict Manson believed would lead to his envisioned societal upheaval.

324. ANSWER: C. LENIENT SENTENCING AND EARLY RELEASE

Gilbert Paul Jordan was able to continue his criminal activities after his release from prison due to lenient sentencing and early release. Despite committing heinous crimes, including multiple murders, Jordan served only six years of his nine-year sentence for manslaughter. This premature release allowed him to resume his killing spree, targeting vulnerable women and exploiting their addictions, thereby

325. ANSWER: C. ANTISOCIAL PERSONALITY DISORDER

Dr. Tibor Bezeredi diagnosed Gilbert Paul Jordan with Antisocial Personality Disorder during a court-ordered psychological examination in 1976. This diagnosis highlighted Jordan's maladjusted conduct in social behavior, his blatant disregard for the rights of others, and his propensity for unlawful activities. The disorder provided a framework for understanding Jordan's relentless criminal behavior and lack of empathy towards his victims.

326. ANSWER: B. MONEY LEFT BY A DECEASED RELATIVE

Gilbert Paul Jordan received a substantial inheritance from his brother Keith, who died of throat cancer in 1976, leaving him $10,000. Instead of using the money to rehabilitate his life, Jordan squandered it on alcohol and further criminal activities. This inheritance enabled him to hire top-tier lawyers, which played a significant role in his ability to evade severe punishment for his crimes, thereby prolonging his spree of murders.

327. ANSWER: C. TO INSPIRE A RACE WAR KNOWN AS "HELTER SKELTER"

Charles Manson orchestrated the murders of Sharon Tate and others with the primary motive of inciting a race war he termed "Helter Skelter." Believing that these brutal killings would be perceived as racially motivated, Manson aimed to provoke societal chaos and upheaval, positioning himself and his followers to emerge as leaders in the aftermath. This delusional plan was rooted in his misinterpretation of The Beatles' song "Helter Skelter."

328. ANSWER: C. BY MATCHING HIS HAIR SAMPLE TO DNA FROM THE VICTIMS

Dennis Rader was ultimately convicted as the BTK Killer by matching his hair sample to DNA evidence collected from the victims. Police obtained a sample of Rader's hair by misleading his daughter into providing it under the guise of needing it to clear his name. The DNA comparison confirmed his involvement in the murders, leading to his arrest, guilty plea, and subsequent sentencing to multiple life terms.

329. ANSWER: B. TESTIMONY FROM SUSAN ATKINS AND LINDA KASABIAN

The chances of indicting Charles Manson's followers for the Tate and LaBianca murders significantly increased due to the testimony of Susan Atkins and Linda Kasabian. Atkins initially agreed to testify against Manson and other Family members in exchange for a lighter sentence, providing detailed accounts of their involvement in the murders. Additionally, Linda Kasabian, who did not kill anyone, testified in exchange for immunity, further solidifying the prosecution's case against Manson and his followers.

330. ANSWER: C. SHE ADMITTED TO SIX KILLINGS

During her trial, Aileen Wuornos admitted to six of her killings, which was pivotal in securing her conviction. Although she denied involvement in the murders of Peter Siems and a John Doe, her confession, combined with physical evidence such as blood-alcohol levels and items found at the crime scenes, was sufficient to convict her. Wuornos' admission played a crucial role in proving her guilt in the heinous crimes she committed against her victims.

CONCLUSION

As we close this chilling expedition into the darkest corners of the human psyche, one haunting truth lingers: the monsters we've encountered are not figments of fiction, but flesh and blood individuals who walked among us. They wore familiar faces, blending into the fabric of society while harboring unimaginable darkness within.

From the "Killer Clown" who lured unsuspecting victims with laughter to the "Vampire of Sacramento" driven by a gruesome thirst, we've peered into the abyss of human depravity. We've learned that evil knows no boundaries, no gender, no age. It can manifest in the charming smile of a Ted Bundy or the grandmotherly guise of Dorothea Puente.

But amidst the horror, we've also witnessed resilience. The brave survivors who escaped the clutches of predators like the Birnies and lived to tell their tales. The relentless investigators who meticulously pieced together fragmented lives, bringing justice to those silenced by violence. And the unwavering families who never relinquished their search for answers, even when hope seemed lost.

Before you go, remember that the world we inhabit is not always safe, not always predictable. The monsters we've encountered in this book may be gone, but their chilling legacy serves as a stark reminder: vigilance is our shield, knowledge our weapon.

The next time you see a discarded toy along a desolate highway, recall the mystery of Asha Degree. When a news anchor vanishes without a trace, remember the haunting case of Jodi Huisentruit. And should you find yourself in a remote cabin or a desolate moor, let the echoes of the Keddie and Moors Murders send shivers down your spine.

For the monsters may be gone, but the stories remain. They whisper in the shadows, reminding us that darkness can lurk even in the most ordinary places. So, keep your eyes open, your mind sharp, and your heart vigilant. The world of true crime is not just a collection of chilling tales; it's a reflection of the human capacity for both unimaginable evil and extraordinary resilience.

THE END...BUT THE STORIES LINGER ON.

Made in United States
Cleveland, OH
01 December 2024

11139535R00090